Whose Choice?

Fortress Books is a socialist publishing house. We encourage our readers to participate actively in the struggle for socialism. If you would like more information about the ideas in this book, or have any comments and suggestions, you are welcome to contact the author via Fortress Books, PO Box 141, London E2 0RL.

Whose Choice?

Working-class women and the control of fertility

Vivien Seal

 FORTRESS

Acknowledgements

The idea for a book on reproductive rights came originally from the Manchester and Liverpool Labour Women's Councils, which have devoted a lot of time to discussing and campaigning on these issues. In writing this book, I have drawn on research on various aspects of reproductive technology which I have been doing, on and off, for twenty years. Much of Chapter 2 is based on my doctoral thesis, but I hope this work, though originally academic, will now have a practical use for working-class women and men struggling for socialism.

Many comrades and friends have contributed to the research and writing of this book. For comments and criticism, editing, technical and historical information, and other work in preparing the book for publication, I would like to thank Margaret Creear, Jane Hartley, Lynn Walsh, Eileen Short, Tony Aitman, Charmian Kenner, Jacky Weiss, Margaret Edwards, Mara Cortesi, Dave Kaplan, Doris and Frank Gee, and Penny Ciancanelli. For their encouragement and support, I would also like to thank Daniel Walsh and Ron Wilson.

Readers who would like more information about the issues covered, or have comments or criticisms, are welcome to write to me via Fortress.

Vivien Seal

Manchester
November 1990

Whose Choice?
Working-class women and the
control of fertility

Vivien Seal

First published November 1990

Text © Fortress Books 1990

Cover design by Alan Hardman

British Library Cataloguing in
publication data:

Seal, Vivien, 1945-
  Whose Choice? : working-class
women and the control of fertility.
1. Family planning. Legal aspects
2. Title
342.448

  ISBN 1-870958-08-X

Published and distributed by
Fortress Books
PO Box 141 London E2 0RL
(081 985 7394)

Printed in Great Britain by Biddles Ltd
of Guildford and Kings Lynn

Contents

Contents

Introduction

Legislation on human infertility treatment and embryo research was passed by Parliament in June 1990, in the form of the Human Fertilisation and Embryology Act, or Embryo Act for short. More than five years ago the issues covered by this legislation were the subject of a Committee of Enquiry headed by Mary Warnock. Following the Warnock Report, and after a further Consultation Document and a White Paper, Parliament was presented with a choice. One option, the one that was carried, was based on the Warnock Report and required the establishment of an independent statutory licensing authority to license clinics offering *in vitro* fertilisation (fertilisation of a human egg outside the body, or IVF), treatment for infertility, and to license establishments storing or carrying out research on human embryos, with a maximum of 14 days after fertilisation for the research. The other option would have been a complete ban on research.

At the same time, opponents of abortion took advantage of the introduction of this legislation to launch yet another attack on the time limit for abortion by proposing amendments to the Bill. On balance, however, the result was a defeat for the anti-abortionists. Although a reduction to 24 weeks in the time limit for most abortions was passed, the anti-abortionists' amendments proposing reductions to 18, 20 or 22 weeks were defeated. The time limit has been removed altogether where pregnancy seriously and permanently threatens a woman's mental or physical health, and also in cases of foetal abnormality. Abortion is discussed more fully in Chapter 3.

Why is Reproductive Technology a Political Issue?

Why should the labour movement take up issues such as contraception, abortion and treatment of infertility, which

are often seen as purely *personal* questions? We believe
that decisions about whether or not to have children,
how many to have, whether or not to have an abortion
or to use any of the technologies available to overcome or
by-pass infertility, or to avoid having a handicapped child,
are all personal decisions to be taken by the individuals
concerned and not by the Church, the state or the medical
profession. Since it is women who give birth to children and
at present bear the main responsibility for childrearing,
these decisions must primarily be theirs. Naturally, in most
cases, women as far as possible share such decisions with
their partners. As socialists, we argue for women to have
the maximum choice possible in the decisions that shape
their lives.

We are not just campaigning for legal rights, but for the
practical means to realise them. In order for a working-
class woman to have the choices already available to rich
women, she must have the economic means (a living wage
or income), and necessary social arrangements, such as
child care and decent housing, so that she can choose to
have a child. It means expanding the NHS and running it
democratically, so women can have access to free and safe
abortion, contraception and infertility treatment. It means
carrying out research to find contraceptives that meet the
needs identified by both women and men; research to
enable women to have earlier abortions and make them
safer; research into causes of infertility and its prevention;
research into chromosomal and genetic disorders and their
prevention; and research into products and services that
would improve the lives of disabled people. All these
things are entirely reasonable and technically possible:
but they raise a number of important, essentially political
questions.

Research aimed at improving contraceptives, for example, immediately raises the questions: who does the research
and in whose interests? The rubber goods manufacturers
and the drug industry do most of the research at the
moment, to make a profit. The drug industry is one of
the more research-intensive sectors: but it spends more on
marketing and advertising than on research. Pressure to be
first to the market with new drugs can lead to corner cutting
in testing: the most notorious case where this happened
was Thalidomide (which was a tranquilliser and sleeping
pill that had been declared safe for pregnant women,

but caused major deformities in their babies, particularly loss or severe deformation of limbs). The manufacturers did not test for foetal defects, although it was known by then that some drugs could have such effects, because it was not specifically a legal requirement. Similarly, the search for profits leads manufacturers to conduct research primarily to find new commodities which will sell in the marketplace.

The Warnock Report commented on the lack of research into the causes of infertility. Five years later this neglect continues, since the results of such research would almost certainly lead to demands for better health and safety at work; and for the replacement of industrial processes, chemicals and other materials causing infertility. These demands would threaten profits. Similarly, research into the causes of infertility would raise questions about the under-funding of the NHS and the number of diseases which are not adequately diagnosed or not adequately treated and which lead to infertility.   The issue of women's rights in reproduction is therefore *a political and a class question*, not just because it is mainly working-class women who are affected by lack of choice and unsafe working conditions, but also because the ability of all women to have a real choice will only be possible as a result of the struggle of working-class women and men to change society. This means campaigning on reproductive rights as well as on better housing, higher wages and defence of the NHS. But especially, it means that we must control the resources of society and organise them for need instead of profit.

1. Ideology and reproductive rights

Reproductive technology is a political issue. The debate triggered off by the government's proposals for legislation to regulate this technology inevitably touches on controversial and emotive issues, especially the role of women and the family and the rights and wrongs of attempts to control human reproduction. When justifying their policies, Tories often claim to be defending 'natural' relationships and 'eternal' moral values.

Far from expressing the needs and aspirations of the majority of people, however, the views put forward by the Tories on these supposedly 'non-political' issues reflect the system of society which they uphold. Capitalism means the exploitation of the working class by a tiny minority who hold the wealth and power in society and pursue their greed for profit through the anarchy of the market. The super-exploitation of women has always been part and parcel of capitalism. Women bear the main burden of raising children, largely in the isolation of the home, with totally inadequate incomes and support from society. Despite the big increase in women working in the post-war period, through which they have gained more income and independence, women still suffer from systematic discrimination at work, in education and in most other spheres. Traditional views – or prejudices – about the 'proper place' of women and the 'natural role' of the family, while claiming to be based on higher moral values, really seek to justify the present position of women and perpetuate their second-class status in the capitalist order of things.

A section of the Tory Party, particularly right-wing Thatcherites, seized on the issue of embryo research (which they have also linked to abortion) as a golden opportunity to stir up fears about the erosion of moral values and the breakdown of civilised standards. Faced with growing opposition to Thatcher's assault on working-class living standards, the welfare state and democratic rights, the Tories are desperately trying to drum up support by drawing on the murky reservoir of reactionary ideas, traditional moral convictions, old-fashioned habits of thought, religious dogma, and outright prejudices. These are the ingredients of the conservative ideology (discussed more fully later in this chapter under 'The New Right') which the ruling class has cultivated over centuries through the churches, education, newspapers and other institutions. They have always reinforced the domination of property and the power of the state with the promotion of capitalist ideas, beliefs and myths, as a kind of glue to secure mass support for the established order. But the Tories' appeal to highly emotive convictions inevitably clouds the real issue: what are the safest and most effective techniques by which women and men can control their fertility, produce healthy children, and improve their personal relationships and social conditions? The Tories are not primarily concerned with real social problems. They are blatantly waging an ideological battle, attempting to turn sensitive personal and social issues to the political advantage of the big-business interests they represent.

The family

The Tory opponents of embryo research and abortion, quite predictably, present the development of reproductive technology as a 'threat to the family'. This is completely hypocritical. While promoting the myth that they are the 'party of the family', no government has done more than Thatcher's to undermine the position of working-class families. Millions of couples, single parents and children have been thrown into poverty. Since 1979, the number of children living in poverty has doubled. The Tories have refused to increase child benefits and have cut most women's maternity benefits. Cuts in the NHS have led to unnecessary suffering and death for many babies and young children.

Yet the Tories cynically play on the desire of working-class parents for a stable, secure relationship in which they can bring up their children. Parents willingly make enormous sacrifices for their children's future. The Tories exploit the fact that the function served by the institution of the family in capitalist society is obscured by the personal commitment of individuals to what they see as the family – their personal relationships, their children and their close relatives.

To most people, the family, which is formed by their choice of a partner, by their decision to set up a household, and by their having children, appears to have an entirely private, personal character. For most working-class people, the stability of the family is bound up with the desire for fulfilling personal relationships and the aspiration to bring up children in comfortable, secure conditions which ensure that they fulfil their potential and enjoy happy lives.

Nevertheless, the family is also a social institution. However individual households are formed, the social framework of the family and prevailing attitudes about the family are determined by the economic and class relationships of capitalism. For the wealthy, the family is primarily a legal-financial relationship which formalises the ownership and inheritance of property. For the capitalist system, the family has an important role in producing each new generation of workers and, of course, consumers. However, the task of raising children, which is obviously vital for the continuation of society, throws enormous burdens on private resources of individual households. Traditionally, women and children were dependent economically on male 'bread-winners'. This has been changed to some extent by the big increase in the number of women working. In many households, women are now the main or sole bread-winners. But whatever the make-up of households, the main burden of domestic work still falls on women. They provide unpaid services such as child care and care of the sick and elderly which otherwise would have to be provided by the state or paid for privately. Legal and General Insurance estimates that to buy in commercially the unpaid work of women would cost £470 a week per household. Even with the development of nurseries, welfare services, child benefits, and so on, the back-up services provided by the state are completely inadequate. Tory cuts have put more and more strain on the slender resources of individual working-class families.

The traditional family, moreover, has always been seen by the ruling class as another means of maintaining control over society. The father, traditionally the 'head of the household', has been held up as a figure of authority. Acceptance of hierarchical authority in the family is linked to acceptance of the hierarchy of wealth and power in society. Because the idea of the family is surrounded by conservative ideology and prejudice, the family unit, which tends to be inward-looking and isolated, is also utilised by capitalist society as a vehicle for passing on and reinforcing standards and values which serve the interests of the ruling class. 'The family,' Thatcher told the Tory Women's Conference in 1988, 'is the building block of society . . . It encompasses the whole of society. It fashions our beliefs. It is a preparation for the rest of our life.'

There is clearly a glaring contradiction between the idealised Tory myth of the family and the many different types of household in which working-class people and their children actually live. People may choose their partners, but most people are far from having a free choice of employment, housing, and other essentials. The kind of household in which people live is therefore often determined by social and economic factors over which they have little or no control. Many relationships break down, leading to the break-up of households and creating various problems in relation to the care of children. Behind many of the personal reasons for splitting up are stress and conflict caused or aggravated by economic pressures, such as poverty-level incomes, bad housing or homelessness, unemployment, or lack of child care facilities.

The Tories prefer to blame 'lack of respect for the family' or the 'decline of moral standards', and so on. This is very convenient politically. The growth of vandalism and crime, for instance, can be blamed not on unemployment and poverty and the brutal conditions under which many young people are forced to live, but on the 'abdication of parental responsibility' and the 'irresponsible' increase of single-parent families. For example, Tory MP Rhodes Boyson said: 'The intentional one parent family is probably the most evil product of our time. Their increased numbers are the cause of violent crime, football hooliganism, mugging and inner city revolt.' At the same time, holding up 'the Family' as an almost sacred institution provides a perfect justification for cutting back on the welfare state. Not only children and the elderly, but the sick, disabled and the mentally ill can be left in the hands of the family. In practice, this mainly means in the care of women, without pay and without any of the necessary back-up resources. In other words, behind the Tories' high-sounding ideals and grandiose moralising, which they use to manipulate public opinion, lies the vested interest of big business – which values private profit much higher than 'wasteful public spending' on the welfare of workers. In her speech on the family, Thatcher went on to say, 'It is a nursery, a school, a hospital, a leisure centre, a place of refuge and a place of rest . . . And women run it.' She did not say: without pay, in isolation, with soul-destroying drudgery. While the Tories revere the idealised role of wife and mother, they are callously indifferent to the problems faced by women in the real world.

The reality of motherhood

From a million and one sources, women are bombarded with propaganda idealising motherhood and blaming them if their experiences are different. Adverts, novels, newspapers, the TV, and even hand-outs from antenatal clinics show happy, serene mothers and polite, clever, clean, tidy and healthy children. When real life does not live up to this unrealistic image, and when the Tories make it more and more difficult to look after children properly, it is women they have the nerve to blame. Rhodes Boyson's comments are typical of some of the attacks on working mothers and single parents in the media.

Unfortunately for the Tories, however, working-class women are increasingly rebelling against the gross exploit-ation and hypocrisy which lie behind this propaganda. One of the reasons for the growing confidence of women is the large number who have been drawn into the work-force. Women constituted 45 per cent of the employed work-force in 1988. It has been estimated that this will rise to 50 per cent in the next few years. Part of their revolt is the rejection of second class status shown in the many recent struggles for equal pay, an end to discrimination, and against cuts in the services which lift some of the burden from women's shoulders. Another part is the demand to be able to control their own bodies. But the arguments of Rhodes Boyson and others are part of a propaganda campaign which has a wider significance than just an attack on single parents, on women's independence or on 'permissiveness' in general.

The New Right

Over the past ten years, the Thatcher government has led a campaign against the post war 'consensus' of Keynesian economic policies (state intervention in the management of the economy and in welfare provision). Not only have the Tories attacked the welfare state, the health service, local democracy and civil liberties, and privatised public utilities and services. They have deregulated the City of London in order to boost profits and even, in some cases, introduced 'markets' where they did not exist before. They have launched a war of ideas in an attempt to justify their blatantly pro-big business policies and also to strengthen their appeal to the most reactionary sections of conservative opinion, particularly the narrow minded new rich and small business strata who now dominate the Tory constituency organisations in many areas.

Prominent in this war of ideas have been the Tories' virulent attacks on 'socialism', the label they falsely attach to the disastrous policies of past Labour governments. The 1974-79 Labour government bears a heavy responsibility for the Tories' victory in 1979. The Labour leaders' underlying philosophy was that capitalism was here to stay and that a socialist transformation was not on the agenda. Their counter-reforms, wage restraint, attempts to shackle the unions and cuts in the welfare state led to the 'Winter of Discontent' in 1979. The result was to discredit socialism. This stands as a warning to future Labour governments: it is impossible to defend the living and working conditions of working-class people while trying to put a diseased system back on its feet.

Thatcher has continually equated the welfare state with socialism and therefore the need for it to be demolished. But after ten years of continuous attacks by Thatcher, workers – and many middle class people too – have experienced many harsh reminders of the real value of the reforms won by the labour movement in the past. The response of 54 per cent of the working-class women surveyed for the Labour Party in 1988 was to support, not just the NHS or the welfare state, but a socialist society. Thatcher's propaganda may still appeal to more backward sections of society, but in general it has rebounded on the Tories.

The Tories, together with various right-wing 'think tanks', journals and much publicised academics, have also kept up a barrage of propaganda about so-called 'social issues' – like the family, 'law and order' and sexual morality. By making the supposedly 'permissive society' of the 1960s (the period of Keynesian economic policies and social reforms) responsible for today's social problems – drug abuse, violent crime, child abuse, etc. – the Tories are trying to divert attention from the real causes, the social pressures fuelled by unemployment, poverty and growing inequalities of wealth.

The anti-abortion or 'moral' lobby groups are not synonymous with the Tory Party or directly run or controlled by the Tories. Life and SPUC (The Society for the Protection of the Unborn Child) are 'nonaligned'. David Alton MP is a 'liberal'. Mary Whitehouse is critical of the Tories for not emphasising 'moral' issues enough. The Tory government could have given enough time to enable the Alton Bill to be passed but did not. Victoria Gillick might perhaps have succeeded in preventing young women having access to contraception before the age of 16 if the Tories had championed her case more actively when – or before – it got as far as the House of Lords.

Individuals and organisations like those mentioned (who have even more vociferously promoted their conservative views and prejudices since the Tories were elected in 1979) represent a layer of society which includes medium and small business people and shopkeepers, sales reps, accountants and estate agents. These groups are often financed by business interests. For example, property developer Godfrey Bradman donated £250,000 to SPUC and paid for the plastic foetus models delivered to every MP before the vote on abortion time limits in April (a counter-productive measure, since its main effect was to upset secretaries who had had miscarriages). Nevertheless, although not directly controlled by the Tory Party, there is a large overlap between right-wing political views and campaigns against 'permissiveness'. Whitehouse says communism discredits the family and attacks 'morality' by 'pushing pornography, homosexuality and degeneracy'. Rhodes Boyson is a right-wing Tory MP. Enoch Powell, a retired right-wing Unionist MP, notorious in the past for his racism, in 1984-5 spearheaded an attack on *in vitro* fertilisation treatment for infertility and on research on embryos. His colleague Martin Smith MP, in a rare moment of clarity during the debate on the Embryo Bill, said 'Perhaps we are misogynists.' The questions of abortion and embryo research uniquely unite right-wing Northern Ireland Unionists with the hierarchy of the Roman Catholic Church to the extent that they are prepared to share public platforms. Thatcher herself has attacked the 'decline in family and moral values', and made sure the 'lumpen aristocracy' were bussed in to the House of Lords to pass the Local Government Act, restricting sex education in schools and containing the notorious Clause 28 which has, as predicted, encouraged attacks on lesbians and gay men.

In the USA, the link between the 'moral majority' and the right wing of the Republican Party is far closer and more blatant, with the former campaigning actively to whip up support for Bush and especially Reagan in the last three presidential elections. The association between the two is far more consciously expressed, too, and the right wing are openly cynical and manipulative in their intentions. Social issues are used to shore up support for economic policies. The US *Conservative Digest* in 1979 said: 'The New Right is looking for issues that people care about, and social issues . . . fit the bill'. Issues such as gun control, abortion, pornography and crime: 'yes, they're emotional issues, but that's better than talking about capital formation'. In other words, it is hard to build mass support using abstract-seeming economic arguments, but emotive campaigns on so-called 'moral issues' can be used to whip up a right-wing backlash. The issues of abortion, *in vitro* fertilisation and embryology are seen as suitable moral issues, as contraception was in the past.

In Britain, where the Tory leadership and 'moral campaigners' are less obviously linked, it is the propaganda value of campaigns against abortion and 'permissiveness', and 'in defence of the family' which are most important. Life and SPUC, for example, deluge the media, medical profession, MPs and the rest of us with their gory, misleading propaganda attacking the Abortion Act. Many backwoodsmen and women in the Tory Party clearly support them and may be members of such organisations.

The Tory leadership courts their support and encourages them with promises of legislation on the issues dear to them. The Tory government, however, represents the interests of big business, not the suburban middle class whose votes they need. While pandering to the most narrow minded, unenlightened sections of conservative opinion, they nevertheless have to take account of the wider consequences of giving legislative force to the more extreme demands of the 'moral right'. Apart from holding back the development of scientific knowledge and technique in human biology, for instance, a ban on embryo research would be a barrier in the way of the pharmaceutical monopolies and private health firms which are eager to exploit another potentially profitable area of medicine. Moreover, the Tories have to contend with deeply rooted social trends which cannot be manipulated at will by propaganda campaigns or even legislation.

The annual *Social Attitude Surveys* provide evidence that the general trend in society is increasingly to reject reactionary views in relation to women. The right of women to make their own decisions has been championed by an increasing majority of society. The labour movement can play a vital role in counteracting reactionary ideas and in firmly supporting a woman's right to choose. Reactionary ideas should not go unanswered, any more than material attacks on living and working conditions.

The government delayed legislation on the regulation of techniques for human fertilisation and embryology for more than five years after the publication of the Warnock Report, and two years after the White Paper. This is not the same ruthless determination in the face even of doubts from their own supporters that we saw in the imposition of the poll tax, social security reform and so on. Nevertheless, the government has whetted the appetites of reactionary groups to such an extent that they will not be appeased by the reduction of the abortion time limit from 28 to 24 weeks. They will not hesitate to continue their campaigns in the future, no matter what agreements the Tories may think they have reached. In June 1990, only a majority of 14 prevented the re-introduction of time limits that had been abolished in April for foetal abnormality and serious risk to the woman's health, while a further amendment to specify the foetal abnormalities that permitted an abortion was only lost on the deputy speaker's casting vote. Ann

Winterton, secretary of the 'pro-life' group in Parliament, has already said 'We shall be back', while the national director of SPUC, Phyllis Bowman, as soon as she heard the vote, said the campaign to reverse the decisions on embryo research 'starts today'.

The 'sanctity of life'

While a large proportion of the Tory Party enthusiastically use arguments about the 'sanctity of life' in their propaganda against abortion or embryology, their concern about fertilised eggs does not extend to a concern about the quality of life *after* birth. The whole campaign stinks of hypocrisy. Some of the people who campaign for the right to life for the foetus, or the fertilised egg (more than two-thirds of which never become a baby when fertilised in a woman's body in the normal way), also support capital punishment. Out of the MPs who signed an advertisement supporting the Alton Bill saying, 'We've abolished the death penalty for hanging. It's about time we abolished it for him too' (with a picture of a foetus), 70 per cent voted to bring back hanging.

The priorities of the Tories (and the US government) are clearly shown in table 1. While many of them support – and use – propaganda about the sanctity of life in relation to embryos and pre-embryos, they are quite prepared to put a majority of research funds into defence related areas. These funds represent a massive waste of resources and assist in propping-up reactionary regimes, as well as increasing and making more sophisticated the means of destroying both the quality of life and life itself.

The Tories have also weakened health and safety legislation and regulations covering the monitoring of new pharmaceuticals on grounds of cost; they have not yet implemented parts of the Control of Pollution Act passed in 1974; and they have cut the funds of the NHS. All of these actions endanger the lives and health of ordinary people, especially premature babies and those born with operable defects: the very human beings whose survival is supposed to be the object of anti-abortion propaganda. When they condone measures which have such life-threatening consequences, the Tories' high minded concerns about embryo research appear completely hollow. Their professed concern for human life is a cynical manipulation of ordinary people's anxieties about the value of life in a society that appears to be ever more callous, competitive and obsessed with 'getting rich quick'.

The capitalist class and its philosophers, religious leaders and intelligentsia formulate abstract rules of 'right' and 'wrong' apparently independent of social relations and of antagonistic class interests. The idea has long been fostered that morality is above classes. In reality, behind even the most hallowed universal principles are concealed the interests of the ruling class. The most basic rules of civilised society – for instance, 'thou shalt not kill, or steal' – are in practice applied quite differently to the wealthy and to workers. In the past, before the development of an educated mass electorate, the link between morality and property interests was often expressed much more bluntly. Dr Samuel Johnson, for example, an 18th century writer, pronounced that 'the chastity of women is of the utmost importance, as all property depends on it' (though 'chastity' is now superseded by 'marriage', at least in the advanced capitalist countries).

The abstraction of 'the sanctity of human life' gives the embryo, from the moment of conception, human status equal to – or in practice, greater than – that of an adult woman. The right of the foetus, which is treated as a completely abstract right and elevated above all real life conditions and problems, is then used as a weapon against the rights of women over reproduction. This is done not just in the case of abortion but also in relation to women's decisions about medical intervention in childbirth or their life-style while pregnant. It is easy to see, therefore, how this abstract moral viewpoint is linked closely to a reactionary and authoritarian attitude to the position of women in which their own interests come second and they are restricted as far as possible to the role of 'homemaker'. Their major and over-riding function is to give birth and bring up children and perform without pay jobs like care of the sick, the old and under-fives and the provision of dinners for schoolchildren, which were once paid jobs before the Tory cuts. It is also linked to the employers' need to keep women who do have jobs vulnerable and therefore cheap in the labour market. It is socialists who are the real supporters of human life through campaigns to put the quality of life and the needs of human beings before profits.

Victorian values

Thatcher has called for a return to 'Victorian values', linking Tory propaganda about the family and the evils of 'permissiveness' to their aim of a return to a market economy with minimum government intervention. In reality, there was no universal set of values accepted by the whole of Victorian society and independent of class interests.

Victorian reality was far from the 'golden age' that Thatcher suggests. The values promoted by the church and ruling class in Victorian Britain, now revived as 'ideal', included an emphasis on chastity, the family and respect for authority and the teachings of the established Christian church. They were also the values of 'self help', individualism, competitiveness and business success – with voluntary 'Christian charity' to help some of the victims of the system if they were seen as 'deserving'. Most capitalists combined naked greed with sanctimonious hypocrisy, even though some campaigned against slavery and child labour.

Workers experienced, not Christian charity and brotherly love, but the most obscene violence and oppression in the factories and slums at home, and even worse in the subjugation of other countries. Women were expected to be chaste and obedient and were shunned by respectable society if they 'fell' from this ideal, facing the workhouse or prostitution for economic survival. Nevertheless, working class women and girls suffered sexual abuse and were given venereal diseases (in epidemic proportions) rather than 'Christian' respect from factory owners, foremen, landlords and others with power over them. Protection of 'chastity' was also used as an excuse to segregate women into low paid 'female' occupations.

The values adopted by the working class were based on the spread of socialist ideas and labour and trade union organisation in the most barbarous period of the industrial revolution – when, for example, life expectancy in the Spitalfields area of London was only seventeen years. They had to fight against child labour, slum housing and drainage that caused cholera epidemics, food adulteration, air thick with hydrochloric acid and other pollution and all manner of workplace hazards. It was not the Christian moral values of the capitalists that gave them reforms.

The working class had to fight for its own morality in which the interests of individual workers are bound up with the common interests of the class as a whole. Loyalty to the organisations built up by the workers through struggle, solidarity with anyone in conflict with the bosses, and mutual co-operation in overcoming everyday problems were vital, living principles. The self-interest of individual workers can only be properly understood and safeguarded when it is linked to the struggle of the labour movement to defend workers against exploitation and oppression and to achieve a socialist society. Conflict between the individual and society 'as a whole' – inevitable when society is based on exploitation and class rule – can ultimately be removed only by changing society so that it is democratically run at every level by the working class in the interests of all. Attempts to secure social harmony through a return to the romanticised standards and moral norms of capitalism's 19th century heyday are futile. It is not at all to 'Victorian values' that we need to return but to the values of the pioneers of the labour movement who rejected the self-seeking ideas, arrogant imperialism, and hypocritical moralising of the ruling class and dedicated themselves to the struggle to abolish capitalism.

Eugenic theories

Opponents of embryo research and of abortion for foetal abnormality claim that such activities will lead to the breeding of a 'master race'. They accuse supporters of women's rights of promoting or at least opening the door to 'eugenics'. Eugenics is the theory of improving human 'stock' by selective breeding, just as animal and plant breeding are routinely done. In other words 'inferior' races and classes would be prevented from breeding too rapidly. Since the proponents of eugenics have almost always been white and wealthy, it is clear who they would encourage to breed.

The word 'eugenics' is rarely mentioned now. This is because eugenics, at least in its crudest and most

explicit form, became discredited by the policies of
Hitler and the Nazis. They sterilised 350,000 people
because they were 'mentally deficient, schizophrenic,
manic depressive, severely deformed and hereditarily
deaf, blind or alcoholic'. Alongside the millions of Jews
murdered during the holocaust were the mentally and
physically handicapped, gay men, gypsies and 'subversives'
like socialists, trade unionists and even surrealist painters.

But eugenic ideas are still being advanced, even though
they are no longer termed 'eugenic'. In 1974, for example,
Keith Joseph expressed essentially a eugenic argument
when he said, 'Our human stock is threatened . . . a rising
proportion of children are being born to mothers least
fitted to bring children into the world . . . Many of these
girls are unmarried . . . deserted or divorced . . . most
of low educational attainment . . . Yet these mothers, the
under-20s in many cases, single parents from classes four
and five, are now producing a quarter of all births.'

Birth control was seen by many of its early supporters
as an ideal method of implementing eugenic policies. The
secretary of the Eugenics Society, CP Blacker, for example,
was also the secretary of the Birth Control Investigation
Committee in the 1920s and 1930s. Propaganda was aimed
at the middle class who thought they were paying too much
in tax in support of poor families with large numbers
of children. Some of the most famous and courageous
campaigners for birth control such as Marie Stopes also
supported eugenic arguments.

On the other hand, the fact that some birth control
campaigners relied on eugenic arguments was used by
some of the Labour leaders as an excuse for not supporting or even opposing birth control reforms. They were not
prepared to challenge the traditional attitudes and prejudices aroused by the issue. They argued that birth control
was a diversion from the struggle for social change (rather
than being part of it); that it would be used by the ruling
class to decide who should and should not have children;
and that it was a way to avoid providing decent wages,
housing, education, health care and so on. In practice, this
meant that they were both unable to stand up to the pressures from the ruling class and fight for decent conditions;
and unable to distinguish between the *reactionary* reasons
of the ruling class for birth control, and the *progressive*
reasons of the working class for campaigning for women to

choose the number of children they wanted, in the interest of women's own health and control over their own lives.

The Labour leadership allowed its justified opposition to eugenics to cloud the issue of birth control. But the thousands of working-class women active in the Women's Labour League challenged the reactionary 'moral' and the apparently more progressive anti-eugenic opposition to birth control in the labour movement.

Conventional history gives the impression that improvements were brought about solely by the campaigns of enlightened middle-class individuals. Certainly Marie Stopes and others fought courageously, and successfully publicised the demand for birth control. But, as even the history of the Family Planning Association says, 'the birth control campaign was led primarily by Labour Women' (Audrey Leathard: *The Fight for Family Planning*). They clearly distinguished between population control in the interests of the rich and the right of women to choose if and when to have children. Labour Women took up the struggle for birth control as part of the class struggle, challenged the ideas of the leadership in the labour movement, and were able to cut across the reactionary ideology of the ruling class and win.

The present campaign on *in vitro* fertilisation and embryology has many lessons to learn from this earlier struggle (more fully described in Chapter 2). Recently, the Labour leadership have at best had an equivocal position on the issue and refused to allow Labour's Annual Conference to discuss policy on it, despite the imminence of legislation. Jo Richardson was one of the few leading Labour MPs even backing the moderate recommendations of the Warnock Report, while Roy Hattersley has expressed strong opposition to many of them.

Television programmes (e.g. *First Born*), radio and press coverage have played on people's fears of the potential for misuse of scientific and medical research and the likelihood of it getting out of control, while the moral right and even some feminists have portrayed embryo research and some applications of *in vitro* fertilisation as the means of implementing eugenic policies, and embryology as even the beginnings of Nazi-style experiments.

The Nazis were only able to implement their eugenic policies and carry out grotesque experiments on human beings in concentration camps because the organisations of the working class had been smashed and therefore no opposition could be organised against them. But this only happened after the labour movement had had several opportunities to take control of society. Practical detection of hereditary diseases and the use of reproductive technologies cannot lead to fascism by the back door. Totalitarian dictatorship will only succeed again if the working class fails to seize the opportunities it will be presented with to carry through the socialist transformation of society.

A group of feminists called FINRRAGE (Feminist International Network of Resistance to Reproductive and Genetic Engineering), whose views were circulated by the Labour Women's Organisation in the Socialist International Women's Bulletin, argue that allowing women not to have children with hereditary diseases is one step along the road to breeding a race of 'perfect' children or 'super-heroes' – the stated intention of the Nazis. They say it also devalues the people who have already been born disabled or who become disabled through accidents and is likely to encourage discrimination against them.

But there is no automatic connection between, on the one hand, offering a woman who will bear the responsibility of giving birth to and rearing a handicapped child the choice as to whether or not she goes ahead with the pregnancy, and, on the other hand, discrimination against disabled people. We would argue that *she* should be the one to make the choice, and that she should be given every support and counselling in doing so. She should not be pressurised to decide one way or the other, but if she decides to go ahead with the pregnancy, the practical facilities for both the disabled child and the parent/s to lead as full a life as possible must be provided.

FINRRAGE also attack *in vitro* fertilisation as a misallocation of resources into high-tech methods of bypassing infertility rather than researching, for example, its causes. Of course, we want both. They argue that women have been conditioned into believing that motherhood at any price is their one true fulfilment as women. Whether the overwhelming desire of some women to have children is entirely a matter of cultural conditioning or is partly hormonal has not been established. However, even if it is entirely socially determined, it is a very real desire which cannot simply be argued away. And to argue that women

are incapable of making a rational choice or fighting
the abuse of power puts a feminist organisation like
FINNRAGE in the same camp as all those who want to
restrict the choices available to women.

Misgivings about research

It is not surprising, however, that there is considerable
public concern about the possibility of misusing research in
the field of human reproduction. Such concern is justified.
Recent poisoning from food and water supplies, radioactive
leaks, sewage contaminated beaches, drugs with serious
side effects and other scandals have not boosted public
confidence in private enterprise's willingness to do research
that will protect our health, or the government's willingness
either to make them or to do it themselves.

In a general sense, technological change is strongly
influenced by the nature of the particular society in which
it develops, so that, for example, industry attempts to direct
research and development towards the goals of increasing
productive efficiency or meeting the anticipated demands
of 'the market'. Even where research is not carried out
by companies, industry can have an important influence
by supplying research funds, employing academics as
consultants, developing their ideas into commercially
exploitable innovations, or even creating a climate in
which certain questions are of dominant importance while
others are marginalised or not posed.

However, there are times when technology develops
such a logic and momentum of its own that it outstrips the
ability of the institutions of capitalist society to deal with
it. Thus, as we shall see in Chapter 2, the development
of hormones which could be used as contraceptives was
far in advance of the ability of the law, official opinion,
government policy or the prejudices of the medical profession to cope with it. Consequently, there was a delay of
twenty-two years after a contraceptive pill became technically
possible before one was launched commercially.

In the case of *in vitro* fertilisation and the discovery of various tests for inherited diseases, as a result
of the development of embryology over the last twenty
years, technology has again made possible various medical

techniques before capitalist laws, policies or ideology have been modified or extended to deal with them.

Reproductive technology now exists. It cannot be *un*discovered by turning the clock back. Fears about the misuse of these techniques cannot be answered by banning them, but only by their being democratically controlled. They are either going to be controlled by us for our own benefit or they will be used by private businesses to make money out of us and threaten our well being. They cannot be independent of class society.

Government Research and Development Spending, by Objective (OECD figures 1986).

	Economic objectives, ie the search for profitable commodities	Defence and space	Health, welfare and the advancement of knowledge
France	27.9%	38.0%	34.1%
W. Germany	30.8%	17.0%	52.2%
UK	18.6%	54.6%	26.8%
USA	9.3%	74.9%	15.8%

2. The struggle for birth control

Early contraceptives

Scientists and doctors did not invent birth control. It was invented by ordinary women and was part of the folk culture of many early societies. It was developed by trial and error and used when the community could not cope with babies – for example when nomadic tribes were on the move. Some early contraceptives – such as the crocodile dung used by the Ancient Egyptians as spermicide – would have been effective at reducing the birth-rate for the community, if not 100 per cent certain to work for individual women. Contraceptives were used, together with abortion, infanticide and abstention. It is clear that none of them was illegal or considered immoral.

Birth control was suppressed in Europe in the Middle Ages as one consequence of the witch-hunts. The church, the feudal lords and the emerging medical profession (a by-product of the monasteries) joined forces in accusing of witchcraft the women healers and midwives who developed herbal remedies for a range of illnesses and provided birth control. The autonomy of these women threatened their control and authority. In Africa and Asia, birth control continued to be practised until imperialism destroyed traditional community life.

By the nineteenth century, the taboo associated with birth control in the industrial countries was part of the general ideology promoted by the church, the state and the medical profession. Social and economic conditions ensured the continued evolution of birth control, even though the technology was backward and the practice illegal. By 1880, there was a greater variety of contraceptives available than in 1960 but black market conditions ensured that profits were huge, quality was low, and the supply of contraceptives was riddled with quackery and false claims about effectiveness. They were bought by the middle class and rich who could afford them. The working class continued to use withdrawal, infanticide and abortion, especially abortion, until well into the 20th century.

These 'pre-industrial' methods were responsible for the decline, for example, in the US birthrate from the highest in the world in the eighteenth century to the second lowest by the end of the nineteenth. In most countries and for most women, abortion was the main method of birth control, even though the penalties were severe and the conditions horrifying. In the 1890s, a US judge estimated that 100,000 abortions were carried out every year in New York City alone (about thirteen times the present rate of legal abortions in Britain), and two million throughout the country. Six thousand of those New York women died – but the death rate from pregnancy and childbirth was higher.

The demand for effective and cheap contraceptives escalated, partly as a result of the publicity given to early campaigners who were prosecuted under anti-birth control laws in the USA or the obscenity laws in Britain. Annie Besant and Charles Bradlaugh, for example, were prosecuted in Britain in 1877 for making the same birth control advice available to working-class women for sixpence that wealthy women were already buying for a few shillings.

Industrialisation

The contraceptive industry became industrialised along with the production of most other commodities: the vulcanisation of rubber revolutionised birth control as well as road transport. The industry continued to grow. By the 1930s, American women were paying $210 million a year for contraceptives, while according to a survey in Britain, they had become almost universal amongst the 'business class'. Working-class women, however, were still relying on illegal and dangerous back-street abortions: less than half the working class was practising birth control, and of those that did, fewer than 60 per cent used 'appliances'.

The industry spent vast amounts on advertising ($935,000 a year in the USA) – which was also illegal – but next to nothing on research, testing, quality control or even market research. They certainly did not look for any new methods of birth control. It was not until the 1950s that there were relatively acceptable contraceptives, tests and clinical trials. The Pill was the first new method in eighty years and it was introduced by the drug industry, not the traditional contraceptive manufacturers.

Research on contraceptives by progressive scientists *outside* the industry was more or less outlawed before the Second World War. The birth control movement raised money to pay a chemist by the name of Baker at Oxford University to work on chemical spermicides. He was constantly being thrown out of laboratories by indignant professors and would put his apparatus and chemicals on a handcart and push it round looking for a department that would let him have a corner of a laboratory in which to work. Even basic research and teaching on the biology of human reproduction was discouraged by the taboo which surrounded anything to do with sex.

Doctors were also strongly opposed to birth control and very few were prepared to make information or supplies available, let alone carry out clinical trials. They also campaigned against anyone else doing so. Yet the British Census of 1911, for example, shows that they were the occupational group which used contraceptives earliest and most widely.

It was 1974 before contraceptive advice and supplies became available in Britain free of charge to all who wanted them. This was the result of decades of struggle, especially by working-class women. Even in 1974, the funding of clinics was inadequate. Now the clinics themselves are threatened by Tory cuts.

In 1989, the Margaret Pyke Centre in London, which trains the majority of GPs for family planning qualifications and deals with 40,000 patient visits a year, was threatened with cuts of £97,000, one-third of its funding, by the District Health Authority (DHA). Nationally, the Family Planning Association estimates that 25 per cent of DHAs have reduced their clinic funding. Cambridge and Trafford District Health Authorities have both put forward plans to close their clinics completely.

The birth control movement

The birth control movement, which was most active during the 1920s and 1930s, campaigned for doctors to prescribe contraceptives, for the state to provide clinics and for legislation where birth control was illegal. They set up and organised most of the clinics, evaluated contraceptives, publicised birth control and raised funds for research. The research was on effective chemical spermicides and even on the effect of hormones on fertility. This was thirty years before the drug industry began to do research on hormones for contraceptive purposes, and when it was only just emerging as a brand new field of science.

Today, the Family Planning Association is considered very respectable. But the equivalent organisations of the 1920s and 1930s were attacked by the press, politicians and doctors in the same way and using the same language as the campaigns for women's rights to abortion still are today. Doctor Hannah Stone and nurse Margaret Sanger, the best known campaigners in the USA, had articles refused by medical journals as 'sensational contributions from fanatical propagandists and hysterical ladies'.

Promoted by the Malthusian League, which believed that overpopulation was the cause of poverty, large open air meetings took place in the Bermondsey area of London in 1921 demanding birth control. Hundreds of working-class people, especially women, attended. As a result of this campaign, London's second family planning clinic was opened in East Street. Women and staff met opposition from the Catholic Church and were pelted with eggs, stones and apples. Windows were smashed and the walls daubed with graffiti such as 'whores'. The clinic was a great success. The Roman Catholic Bishop of Salford called on his flock to smash the Manchester, Salford and District Mothers' Clinic set up in 1926. Bricks were thrown through the window, but the resulting publicity only encouraged the attendance of women who did not already know about the clinic.

The labour movement

The struggle for birth control was a bitter one. At the height of it, the labour movement was split on the issue. Some opposed birth control on religious grounds. Some said it was a personal and not a political matter. And many used their opposition to eugenics as an excuse to oppose birth control, as mentioned in Chapter 1. These are very similar reasons to those given today by some people in the labour movement for opposition to abortion or the use of embryo research for diagnosing genetic disease.

It was the Labour Women's Organisation that refused to be diverted by eugenicist issues and which spearheaded the campaign for the labour movement to support birth control and for the government to fund the clinics to provide it. Working-class women were the backbone of the Labour Party between the wars. Although they were even less represented on the leading bodies than today and the leadership tried to discourage them from discussing general political matters, they nevertheless formed an active body, the Women's Labour League (WLL), which campaigned especially on issues concerning working-class women. There were 100,000 in women's sections in the 1920s and nearly twice as many in the 1930s.

Working class women's lives consisted of hours of drudgery. Seventeen hours a day of heavy housework was common: hauling coal and water upstairs and ashes and dirty water downstairs, cooking, cleaning and washing by hand. When workers in the household were on shift work, they came home in relays, creating a continual round of meals and clearing up from dawn to midnight. *Labour Woman*, reviewing the Ideal Home Exhibition, showed that very few, if any, of the labour-saving devices beginning to be introduced at that time were within the means of working-class families. Even when members of the family were in full-time work, working-class families could not afford a very nutritious diet. Women often went hungry to feed the others. When no one was in work the situation became desperate. An extra pregnancy could push the family over the line between survival and destitution. Thousands of women were driven by exhaustion and desperation to back street abortionists. In the first three months of opening her clinic to offer contraception, Marie Stopes had 20,000 requests for abortions.

Between 1900 and 1932, the birth and death rates for Britain fell. Infant mortality fell from 142 to 68 per 1000 live births. But maternal mortality rates continued to rise from 3.91 per 1000 in 1921 to 4.12 in 1926 and 4.33 in 1929. Working-class women were normally exhausted, overworked, undernourished and suffering from chronic ill-health. Standing led to varicose veins and swollen legs and ankles. Lifting led to backache and uterine prolapse.

Damp conditions meant rheumatism and arthritis, while poor sanitation led to constipation. These were the routine ailments suffered by working-class women and considered 'normal'. On top of all that came pregnancy and childbirth. The National Insurance Scheme did not cover anything connected with childbirth and women were in any case excluded from it unless they had paid work themselves. Most jobs required women to leave on marriage; married women were only a significant proportion of the work-force (23 per cent) in the textile industry.

The Labour Women's Organisation

The Women's Labour League was mainly made up of women who suffered from these conditions and campaigned especially on prices, housing and health. From 1924 onwards, the Labour Women's Conference annually and unanimously supported birth control. In 1924, too, the first Labour government was elected with John Wheatley as the first Labour Minister of Health. The Women's Labour League bombarded the Minister with demands for improved maternal health and the provision of free, state birth control clinics. They organised meetings and major demonstrations. They kept reminding him that giving birth had four times the death rate of working in the mines, the most dangerous job for men, and twenty times the likelihood of permanent disablement.

Labour controlled boroughs began to provide birth control. The opening of the Bermondsey clinic, together with five municipal infant welfare centres and a slum clearance programme by the left-wing Labour council, led to a vast improvement in infant mortality rates which fell from 102 per 1000 in 1922 to 67 per 1000 in 1927. Maternal mortality rates fell to one of the lowest in London, below that of the West End and suburban boroughs. Other Labour boroughs followed, with Battersea and Stepney providing family planning and infant welfare clinics in 1924.

Although John Wheatley was a left-winger from Red Clydeside, responsible for the only major gain of the first Labour government, a Municipal Housing Bill, he was also a Catholic. He took a religious rather than a class attitude. He therefore threatened to withdraw their grants.

Circular 517, dated 30 June 1924, officially instructed local authorities to give no contraceptive information to any mother in any circumstances. Deputations of Labour women descended on Wheatley.

The Labour party officially continued to oppose birth control or refuse to discuss it as 'not a party-political issue'. A Private Member's Bill in favour of birth control was defeated by two to one in Parliament in 1926, with 44 Labour MPs voting against it. In response to the solidarity shown them by Labour women during the General Strike, however, several branches of the Miners' Union supported their campaign for birth control. The Durham Miners' Welfare Committee, for example, donated £100 to help the Newcastle clinic open in 1929.

The second Labour government finally gave in to the 'irresistible and irreversible pressure' from all sides, led by Labour women. In 1930, the new Minister for Health sent local authorities a typed memorandum 153/MCW, allowing them, if they chose, to provide birth control at child welfare clinics – though only to married women for whom further pregnancy would be a health hazard. By the 1940s, over 40 per cent of married women were estimated to be using contraception some of the time. At the end of the Second World War, the upsurge in working-class aspirations and militancy led to a landslide victory for Labour in 1945. They brought about major reforms, which, along with the growing use of contraceptives, led the Royal Commission on Population in 1949 to recommend that the new National Health Service should provide birth control to anyone who wanted it, even if it was not a medical necessity. The recommendation eventually was fully implemented more than twenty years later.   The Labour Women's Organisation had cut across the ideology of the ruling class and successfully campaigned on a class basis for the provision of birth control. No one should underestimate the importance of the reforms which led to the provision of birth control, however inadequate that provision and quality might be. The ability of women to control the number of pregnancies they had, along with improvements in diet, housing and the establishment of the NHS, led to a vast improvement in women's health. Much still needs to be done in the labour movement, especially in relation to the provision of care for dependants. But the freeing of women from continuous pregnancy and childrearing has contributed to the combativity of recent generations of women and their ability to participate more actively and consistently in the class struggle.

The drug industry

In the 1950s, drug firms acknowledged that they were doing research on hormonal contraceptives, although they had been researching hormones since the 1920s and 30s. In 1938 a drug firm had synthesised a chemical that worked like the synthetic hormone which eventually appeared in the Pill in 1960. Yet no patent or scientific paper – apart from the work of one group at Edinburgh University sponsored by birth control movement funds in the 1920s – said anything about using hormones for contraception. Drug firms were doing research on hormones to be used for infertility, arthritis and muscle building. But all these hormones, like those eventually used in the Pill, had a similar chemical structure (they were steroids), and could be applied to birth control when it became 'respectable' to do so.

Researchers were strongly influenced by the fact that birth control was a taboo subject. In America it was still illegal and in Massachusetts, where a lot of the research on hormones was done, it was not legalised until 1964, four years *after* the Pill's launch. Drug firms were particularly concerned with their 'respectable' professional image, associated with the prestige of science and wanted to distance themselves from the seedy, under-the-counter, 'dirty raincoat' image of the traditional contraceptive manufacturers. This was for reasons purely to do with their profits, as a spokesman from GD Searle made clear: 'The possibility of losing overnight one-fourth of our personnel, a considerable portion of our hospital business and a crippling number of the physician prescribers of our products was not to be contemplated lightly.' The first Pill was launched by GD Searle in 1960 in the USA. What made them decide to put it on the market, when they had been so recently afraid that it might damage their business? First of all, they were aware of a massively increased demand for birth control. The post-war boom meant that most working-class as well as middle-class families increased their standard of living. For the first time, mortgages, cars, electrical goods, holidays and so on, were within their grasp and there was a strong incentive to limit the number of children in order to make the family budget stretch. Related to this was a rise in the number of women going out to work, made up largely by the massive increase in married women and mothers in the work-force. A similar increase in the numbers of women in further education also took place. All these women were demanding an effective means of planning whether or when to have children. The same development led to a conflict between the hierarchy and the working-class members of the Catholic Church. In the battle between material necessity and religious loyalty, material necessity won. By 1967, almost as many women from a Catholic background (80.3 per cent) as from the rest of the population (94.5 per cent) were using birth control.

Companies like GD Searle realised they had in their laps the classic golden egg of the drug business – a pill to be taken not by the sick but by the healthy, and by millions of women almost every day throughout their child-bearing lives. At the same time, a massive change in the official view towards birth control on the part of the government, doctors and scientists and that put across by the mass media, took place as a result of the 'population explosion'. This new climate of opinion was used by the drug industry to legitimise their work on contraception.

The 'population explosion'

Capitalism was unable to take society forward in the colonial and ex-colonial world. Widespread starvation was suffered by millions of people in those countries not as a result of natural disasters but because food production was controlled by multi-national companies for their own profit. There is enough food produced in the world to feed the whole population on the basis of existing technology. But subsistence agriculture for the feeding of local people was abandoned for the production of food as a commodity, mainly for export. If you could not afford what was left locally, you starved; and if you were still subsistence farming, you were being squeezed by the landlords and money-lenders.

After the Second World War, there was a rapid development of revolutionary movements in the Third World, which threatened the interests of the multinationals. The governments of the industrialised countries responded in some cases with military aid to reactionary regimes or with direct military intervention. Where they thought protests, riots and potential revolutions could be defused by alleviating the worst poverty and starvation, they supplied economic aid. But the cheapest solution of all was to reduce the growth in the numbers of people to feed, using population control programmes. 'Less than $5 invested in population control is worth $100 invested in economic growth', said Robert McNamara, President of the World Bank.

These programmes were accompanied by a great deal of propaganda about the 'population explosion' as the cause of world poverty and the altruism of the US, UK and other governments in doing something about it. It was evidently effective because it is widely believed, even by some in the labour movement. Labour MP David Blunkett, for example, said in the debate on the Embryo Bill in Parliament that he considered over-population to be one of the greatest dangers facing the world, more serious than nuclear war, AIDS or global warming. It had a dramatic effect on government attitudes to birth control: for example, President Eisenhower said of birth control in 1959: 'I cannot imagine anything more emphatically a subject that is not a proper political or governmental activity or function or responsibility.' But six years later he was chairing the honorary sponsors of Planned Parenthood. Even scientific journals had absurd headlines, like *Science Newsletter's* 'The explosive increase in world population could be squelched by a tiny pill.'

Population control was taken up with enthusiasm by some of the reactionary leaders of the Third World. For example, thousands were compulsorily sterilised in India during Indira Gandhi's State of Emergency in 1977-8. We, of course, support the right of women in the Third World to have access to free, safe contraception. But there should be no coercion involved.

GD Searle had no hesitation in using the propaganda to make the company look altruistic, although their target market was the better-off, better-educated, mainly white middle-class women in the USA and the expanding Health Service in Britain, not the Third World at all. By 1964, they were making 38.9 per cent return on investment a year. By 1965, only three per cent of married women in the USA had not heard of the Pill and 26 per cent were taking it. Several other companies which had held back to see if Searle would sink or swim jumped on the bandwagon and produced an array of chemically similar brands. The scientific image of the Pill contributed to the increasing support for birth control among doctors and to freer public discussion of sex, fertility and contraception in general. Even the traditional contraceptive manufacturers were spurred on to improve their quality control, their image and their products.

Side effects

But then came the reports of side effects. First of all effects such as weight gain, nausea and headaches were reported and dismissed as minor by the companies and many doctors, although they were by no means minor to the women who suffered them. Very little testing for side effects was done before the Pill was launched. The US Food and Drug Administration gave it a licence on the strength of just 132 case histories for studying unwanted effects. Most of the early clinical trials were done in Puerto Rico where, the firms believed, women would be grateful for their 'help' and less likely to sue if anything went wrong.

In 1968 came conclusive evidence about just one side effect - thromboembolic disease. The high oestrogen pill was withdrawn, but as is often the case with dangerous drugs, USAID bought them up cheaply for use in the Third World. Since then, the Pill has been regularly linked to increased incidence of breast cancer, cervical cancer, stroke and heart attacks. The scientific journal *Nature* reported in 1986 that there had been a decline in research on safe contraceptives, although a new contraceptive, the 'female condom', was reported in 1988.

Depo-Provera, the injectable contraceptive, has more serious side effects than the Pill. At first banned in the US and UK, it has been widely used in the Third World. An injection given once every three or six months, it appears to have advantages over the Pill which you have to remember to take on certain days. But if it makes you ill, nothing can be done until the effects of the injection wear off. It does, however, give a great deal of control to the administrators of population programmes who rarely give women a real choice or explain the risks or side effects of them. Depo-Provero has now been approved for use in Britain. There have been many reports of its routine use on poor, black, working-class women and on single mothers living on benefits on Glasgow housing schemes.

It is not only birth control drugs which have unwanted side effects. The Dalkon Shield was the largest selling intra-uterine device (IUD) in the world in the 1970s. It was withdrawn from the US market in 1974 and in Britain in 1975 after causing pelvic inflammation leading to sterility and even death. It was then sold in bulk, unsterilised, to USAID at a 48 per cent discount for use in the Third World. Only in 1980 did the manufacturers write to doctors suggesting they remove the shields they had fitted to women before 1974. Finally, in 1985 they agreed to undertake a publicity campaign to alert women to the need to have them removed. About 300,000 women, 3,700 of them in Britain, are trying to get compensation from a now bankrupt company.

The drug companies spend more on advertising than they do on research; they are frequently involved in over-pricing scandals; and several tragedies, such as the Thalidomide, Opren (a drug for arthritis which killed several elderly patients), and Practolol (a 'beta blocker' heart drug withdrawn by ICI as a result of serious side effects) disasters have been caused by inadequate testing and delays in withdrawing products suspected of causing serious side effects. Labour Women have consistently called for the public ownership of the pharmaceutical industry under workers' control and management and its integration into the NHS.

Contraceptives are most effective, not only when there is proper provision of them, but also when that provision is linked to counselling services and sex education. When *Woman* magazine did a survey in the early 1980s, only one in ten thought that sex education was too explicit. Four out of five said there was too little sex education and half said their own lack of sex education had caused them problems.

Nowadays, the widespread legal availability of contraception is generally accepted. But nothing can be taken for granted. In 1986 Victoria Gillick won a court ruling to prevent doctors from prescribing contraceptives to her daughters without her consent while they were under sixteen. This ruling led to a memo from the DHSS to doctors and clinics, putting birth control for all under-16s in jeopardy. The case got as far as the House of Lords before the ruling was overturned – but not before there had been an increase in unwanted teenage pregnancies. Lord Scarman recognised the earlier social maturity of young people, commenting that, 'The majority of young people are fully able to make sensible decisions about many matters before they reach the age of sixteen.'

We are campaigning for:

* Free, safe contraception which really meets the needs of men and women.
* The reversal of cuts in family planning and the establishment of a sympathetic youth advisory service, to provide help and facilities to deal with the special problems of young people. A third of health authorities have reduced family planning services for cash reasons. In the region covered by of West Lambeth Health Authority, where abortion rates are the highest in the country, three Brook Advisory Service family planning clinics (specialising in providing a service for young people) are to close.
* The right of all young people to sex education in school.
* The public ownership of the pharmaceutical industry. The millions of pounds taken in profits from the NHS every year could be used to restore cuts and for the expansion of services. Drug companies claim no one would take the risks associated with research if they could not make high profits; but the most risky medical research is paid for by government research grants and, increasingly, charity.

3. Abortion — the campaign for the right to choose

While the campaigns on contraception were gathering momentum, abortion was the main method of birth control practised by working-class women. Gradually, court cases, reflecting changes in public opinion, weakened the Offences Against the Person Act, to allow women to have abortions where their mental or physical health was seriously threatened. This meant that wealthy women could get round the law. But most working-class women continued to have back-street abortions, risking their lives and their health and going to prison. In 1937 there were estimated to have been about 150,000 illegal abortions and 411 deaths.

After the Second World War, the number of abortions grew. There were 10,000 legal abortions done privately and 2000 by the NHS. Back-street abortions were a much and 2000 by the NHS; the number of back-street abortions was much higher. That did not mean that women had the became more publicly recognised, the medical profession campaigned to keep it under their control. Abortion was allowed only on medical grounds — that pregnancy would seriously endanger the woman's health and the decision was taken by doctors, not by the woman concerned.

In Romania, abortion was illegal until 1989 under the repressive Ceausescu regime. Illegal abortions, punishable by six years' imprisonment, still outnumbered live births. In 1987, there were 300,000 live births and 1.2 million abortions. In Bucharest, 20,000 women were admitted to hospital with post-abortion complications and 25 per cent were permanently damaged. A woman of 40 would have had, on average, between five and nine abortions. The graves of women who died from botched up abortions were shown on British television news after Ceausescu's overthrow. Their other children were being raised by grandparents. Pictures of victims of illegal abortions, seriously ill in intensive care, were shown next to pictures of long queues for newly legalised abortions.

Just like Romanian women recently, women in Britain before 1967 were not deterred from having abortions because they were illegal. They simply had them under extremely dangerous conditions. Pressure began to build up as more and more women arrived in casualty departments, the victims of botched back-street abortions. In 1965, 3,050 women suffered from post-abortion sepsis. It was not unusual to have whole wards full of women with septic abortions. Private Members' Bills to decriminalise abortion were introduced in 1953, 1961, 1965 and 1966. Finally, in 1967, David Steel's Abortion Bill was passed. The Labour government adopted an attitude of 'benevolent neutrality' to the Bill.

The 1967 Abortion Act

The 1967 Abortion Act was one of the many reforms gained by women in the years of economic boom. Rising employment amongst women and improved living standards for the majority raised their confidence. They demanded recognition for their role in society and the right to control their own lives. This led not only to the Abortion Act but also to Equal Pay and Sex Discrimination legislation.

Clearly abortion was not invented by the 1967 Act, although its opponents often give that impression. The Act made abortion legally and safely available to the mass of women – it decriminalised what women had been doing for centuries. It was only with the 1967 Act that abortions could be obtained on 'social grounds'. This does not mean termination of a pregnancy which would interfere with your social life, as some members of SPUC imply. It means reasons other than the threat of death or serious illness: women who have no job or live on poverty incomes; are homeless or live in over-crowded, damp or high rise flats; who have violent husbands; or who can barely cope with life as it is; or for some other equally serious reason. For women in these circumstances, pregnancy could push them over the edge between survival and nervous breakdown or destitution. In any case, it is impossible to separate social conditions and health. These are the realities of many women's lives, now as in the 1920s.

A serious drawback to the 1967 Act was that no provision was made for extra NHS facilities. A woman's right to choose is meaningless unless linked to an expansion of the NHS and especially of day care facilities to enable more abortions to be done early. In particular, in 1988 the campaign against the Alton Bill and the campaigns to stop the cuts in the NHS should have been drawn together.

The continued rise in the number of abortions carried out after seventeen weeks' pregnancy, from 1317 (January – March 1987) to 1579 (January – March 1988), in spite of SPUC's propaganda, shows the continuing difficulties women face in getting early abortions. The overall abortion rate also rose again, from 13.5 per 1000 women aged 15-54 in 1986 to 14.2 per 1000 in 1987. This really underlines the problems women face under Thatcher's government, making pregnancy and child rearing intolerable for many. Furthermore, in England and Wales, only 44 per cent of abortions were paid for by the NHS. The trend towards using abortion agencies has reached its highest level in the West Midlands, where, in addition to the 17 per cent carried out in the NHS itself, a further 31 per cent are contracted out to agencies but paid for by the NHS. The lack of adequate funding for NHS abortion facilities is encouraging the private sector, just as infertility treatment is being used to introduce more and more private practice (see Chapter 6).

We are told by propaganda that Britain is the 'abortion capital' of the world. Yet eight European countries, including France and Italy, have more liberal laws, with abortion on request up to at least 12 weeks. In Britain you still have to get the permission of two doctors which can lead to serious delays and therefore to late abortions. An amendment to the Embryo Bill to allow abortion on request up to the end of the twelfth week of pregnancy was defeated by a majority of 105. The labour movement must now campaign for this liberalisation to be introduced in future legislation. In Sweden, abortion is available on request up to 18 weeks, with the result that 95 per cent of abortions are carried out before 12 weeks and only 1 per cent after 18 weeks. The countries with the most liberal abortion laws are often those with the best maternity care, child care and parental leave, such as Sweden and

Denmark, where the labour movement has fought for better conditions for women in general. It is no coincidence that Britain is close to the bottom of the West European league in both.

The number of women from other countries coming to Britain for abortions has declined as legislation in those countries has been liberalised. The most striking example is Spain, where abortion was legalised in 1985. The number of Spanish women coming to Britain for abortion halved from 1986 to 1988. The largest group of women coming to Britain from other countries are now Irish women, from both North and South, where abortion is still illegal. From April 1968 to December 1986, 20,957 from the North and 41,548 from the South came to Britain for abortions. Many other Irish women would not be able to find the money to travel to Britain. Yet in the debate in Parliament, when an amendment was moved to extend the legislation on abortion to Northern Ireland, Irish MPs said there was no support for the amendment in Northern Ireland itself. It was particularly nauseating to hear about the 'sanctity of life' from MPs such as Ian Paisley, who have directly or indirectly promoted sectarianism. The campaign to extend the legislation to Northern Ireland must continue. In addition to the assistance this would give to women in the North, it would also put pressure on the South which remains one of the few countries in the world, alongside Chile, to have a constitutional ban on abortions. In Pinochet's Chile, abortion was the single largest killer of women.

At the end of 1989 SPUC took out an injunction to prevent the officers of Trinity and University College Student Unions in Dublin and of the Union of Students in Ireland giving out phone numbers which women seeking advice or information on abortion could contact. After a battle in the courts, when student leaders refused to back down, the right to give information was upheld. This has since been reversed and the fight continues.

The time limit

Recent debates over abortion centred on the time limit of 28 weeks' gestation cited in the Infant Life Preservation Act. Alton's Private Member's Bill in 1988 attempted to reduce the time limit to 18 weeks. In 1990, the government added a new Clause 34 to the Embryo Bill, which was an amendment to the 1967 Abortion Act. In the debate on this clause, the government, playing Russian Roulette with women's lives, allowed amendments which put alternative time limits ranging from 28 to 18 weeks. Parliament voted for a time limit of 24 weeks, in effect backing what the Tories had already established in recent years through ministerial regulations.

Very welcome liberalising exemptions were made to this time limit in cases of 'grave and permanent' damage to the pregnant woman's health, and in cases of foetal handicap, where the time limit was removed altogether. During the debate, the case of Mrs Rance was cited: doctors discovered she had a handicapped foetus so close to the 28 week limit that they did not tell her, knowing she would ask for an abortion. The new legislation should prevent other women going through such an experience. A threat to the mother's life was already an exemption in the provisions of the Infant Life Preservation Act 1929, and this has also been adopted in the clause of the Embryo Act dealing with abortion. Finally, a section was added to the new Act to decouple the Infant Life Preservation Act and the Abortion Act, which will reduce the possibilities of prosecution of doctors by groups such as SPUC.

The legislation is to be welcomed and seen as a victory, considering the intense campaigning by SPUC and Life for a much lower limit. The 24-week limit, however, especially if, in accordance with existing practice, it is actually applied as a 22-week limit, could adversely affect very young women who tend to apply for abortions late and will not be exempted by the new legislation.

The concentration of discussion on time limits is in many ways a diversion from the real problems women confront. Women are not irresponsible or callous. No woman *wishes* to have a late abortion. The later in pregnancy, the more psychological strain there is on the woman during the unwanted pregnancy. Late abortions, moreover, are carried out by the induced still-birth of the immature foetus which any woman would rather avoid. Those who must have later abortions are some of the most serious cases, women who will suffer the most tragic consequences if they are forced to go ahead with an unwanted pregnancy. Records from the Pregnancy Advisory Service of 59 cases of late abortion show that 30 per cent resulted from administrative delays within the NHS; 17 per cent were cases where doctors had failed to diagnose the woman's pregnancy in spite of her own suspicions; and 12 per cent were the result of changed circumstances – usually desertion by their partners.

The main groups of women who are forced to have late abortions are:

1. Women who have to wait for amniocentesis tests (in which a small sample of fluid from the waters around the foetus – the amniotic sac – is extracted to carry out tests for possible genetic defects) to be done because they are at risk of having children with Downs Syndrome, Spina Bifida or various other hereditary and congenital diseases. These tests cannot be done before the sixteenth week of pregnancy. Such women should now be covered by the new exemption.

If SPUC were serious about wanting to end late abortions, they would support embryo research which has made possible tests which can be conducted earlier than amniocentesis. Of course, SPUC are not interested just in stopping late abortions; they want to stop all abortions, as well as embryo research.

2. Very young women who do not realise they are pregnant or are too scared to tell anyone. Recent attempts, like Victoria Gillick's, to get contraception banned for the under-16s without parental consent, although ultimately unsuccessful, have deterred young women from going to contraceptive clinics. Attacks on sex education will further undermine young people's understanding of conception and contraception and their confidence in obtaining and using contraceptives. Both developments will increase the number of young women with unwanted pregnancies.

3. Women who do not realise they are pregnant because they are either going through the menopause or think they are and, at the age of 40-50, possibly with grown-up children already, cannot face the prospect of pregnancy, childbirth and rearing a child until they are pensioners.

4. Women who are delayed by queues for NHS abortions. A large proportion of those having abortions after 18 weeks

had first been to see their doctors before the twelfth week of pregnancy. In the third reading, there was an attempt to liberalise abortion law further by ending the requirement for two doctors' signatures. This would have reduced delays in getting abortions, but it was defeated by just 28 votes. With a more active campaign, this amendment could have been carried. The labour movement must now go on the offensive to ensure this liberalisation takes place in the near future.

If Alton and his supporters had really wanted to reduce post-18 week abortions, he would have supported this amendment and Jo Richardson's earlier Private Member's Bill to extend day care abortion. But they are against *all* abortion.

Although many MPs voted tactically for 24 weeks to prevent greater reductions in the time limit, the government, David Steel and even some MPs who have been strongly pro-choice have recently indicated either support for, or acceptance of, a reduction in the legal limit to 24 weeks. This is based on arguments about the 'viability of the foetus'.

Viability of the foetus

Advances in technology make it possible to keep alive some babies born prematurely. Though babies born after only 23 weeks of pregnancy are believed to have survived, the statistics are not encouraging. The most recent ones available show that at 24-25 weeks 80 per cent of babies die, and at 26-27 weeks 62 per cent die. Of those surviving below the age of 28 weeks' gestation, 25 per cent will have some degree of impairment, half of them a severe one. Where hospitals have resuscitation equipment, it is always on stand-by in cases of late abortions. The possibility of some aborted foetuses surviving with technological intervention should not be allowed to curtail women's abortion rights.

Of course, we support care for very premature babies born before 30 weeks gestation. However, the resources given to this area contrast with a general lack of medical resources for babies (including premature babies born between 30 and 40 weeks, most of whom can survive without damage, given the necessary equipment) and children. For example, statistics show there was an average

3572 special care cots in English hospitals in 1987-88. This was 8.4 per cent down on the average of 3898 in 1983 (during which time the number of births rose by 8.4 per cent) and 10.9 per cent down on the 1977 average of 4007. Over the period from 1983 to 1987/88, the number of hospital beds fell by 13.4 per cent.

No reduction in the time limit

We are opposed to a reduction in the time limit for abortions. SPUC and Life argue that allowing late abortions in cases of foetal abnormality, for which the time limit has been abolished, undervalues disabled people.

We campaign as actively for facilities for disabled people and their families as we do for a woman's right to choose. This is in contrast to Ann Widdicombe MP, a leading SPUC supporter, who voted against the select committee report on social services and community care which recommended greater help for carers. But in the end, and especially in Thatcher's Britain, it is the parents and especially the mother who will have to cope with a disabled child and it must therefore be her choice whether to continue with her pregnancy or not.

Many of the diseases diagnosed after 18 weeks cause the most harrowing and painful deaths of very young children and the most awful suffering for their families. People with hereditary diseases in their families dare not even risk having a child unless they have the option of aborting a damaged foetus. For people to have to choose between the risk of giving birth to a child who will suffer terribly and die young or never having a child at all is not pro-life but profoundly anti-life (this is discussed more fully in Chapter 5 on embryo research). In the 1988 *British Social Attitudes Survey*, 88 per cent were in favour of women being able to choose an abortion in relation to foetal abnormality. Women must not be punished for the inadequacy and delays of the NHS and for late testing. SPUC and Life have already started to campaign for a restoration (and lowering) of time limits of abortion in cases of foetal abnormality.

The new 24-week limit could have a serious effect on young women who may not realise they are pregnant, or who may be too frightened to tell anyone; and on older women who think they are going through the menopause. The Brook Advisory Centre gave an example of an abortion which might now be refused:

> A Bedfordshire girl, Sandra, aged 16, presented herself at a youth advisory clinic when she was 22 weeks pregnant. She was accompanied by an older sister who was 19. Sandra had refused to believe she was pregnant, which is why she had not sought help earlier. Both sisters said their father would kick the girl out of home if the pregnancy were discovered. Since late terminations were unavailable on the NHS, Sandra was told she would have to find £460 for a private charity abortion. Sandra, who was still at school, was going to take on a Saturday job and her sister was going to take on extra temping in order to find the money. Fortunately, the charity which performed the termination trusted the girls and allowed them to pay back the money on a weekly basis.

Brook also gave an example of a 15-year-old who was 23 weeks pregnant and, on the basis of the old legislation, in conjunction with ministerial directives, had been refused an abortion. Such examples show not only that many teenagers are particularly vulnerable to lower time limits: they also demonstrate the cost of increased use of private and charity abortions. These examples also underline the need for an enormous publicity campaign which must now be waged to ensure that young women are aware of the rights they do have, along with the provision of sex education and contraception which would reduce the numbers coming forward for abortions in the first place.

In the debate in Parliament, several further examples were given of women who went to their doctors as early as two weeks pregnant, not realising that these doctors were strongly anti-abortion. As a result of bureaucratic delays, compounded by obstruction from their doctors, these women were unable to have abortions until well after the twentieth week. Under the new legislation, they might not have been able to have them at all.

The 'abortion pill'

The French drug company, Roussel, recently launched an abortion pill, Mifepristone (also called RU 486). It blocks the body's production of the sex hormone progesterone, which is essential to the maintenance of pregnancy, and brings on a heavy period lasting for about twelve days. It may also be used with a suppository or injection of prostaglandin which causes contractions. So far, 95 per cent success rates have been achieved. Roussel were all set to withdraw the pill in October 1989 as a result of pressure from anti-abortion campaigners but the French government insisted on its continued availability. Roussel are presently expected to apply for a licence to market Mifepristone in Britain. One of the reasons for such equivocation in France was that Higler, President of Roussel's parent company, Hoechst, is personally opposed to abortion.

It is a condemnation of so-called 'private enterprise' and its undemocratic character, that one man can, for ideological reasons, delay the marketing of a drug that may prove useful to thousands of women if thoroughly tested. We are totally opposed to the health service being held to ransom either ideologically or financially by overpricing essential drugs to keep profits up.

The abortion pill is currently administered only by doctors. Clearly both counselling and some kind of medical supervision are necessary. Very little has been published about unwanted side effects, although vomiting and diarrhoea seem to be fairly common and the process is painful. The drug industry's safety record indicates that we should not welcome this pill without qualification. At the same time, the possibility of abortion without surgery is a very attractive one. If it proves to be safe and is widely available, it will remove some of the trauma of waiting for an abortion, let alone of the abortion itself. Some official interest has been shown in introducing RU 486 quickly because it will save £15 million for the NHS. But this money must not be cut from the NHS. It must be used to *improve* abortion facilities.

Abortion is a social and emotional, as well as a medical, question. More counselling and help has to be made available to assist women, many of whom will be distressed by having an abortion, even when they feel they have absolutely no alternative.

An abortion pill does not avoid the issue of who decides, however, by making abortion a matter of 'home medicine'. Doctors will still decide whether to prescribe the drug and

the state will decide whether to let them, quite aside from
the question of safety. A woman's right to choose will still
have to be fought for and Life and SPUC are already
campaigning against it with gory images – this time of
'chemical war'. The likelihood, however, is that the abortion pill, if safe and widely available, will defuse the whole
issue of abortion and time limits. It will be possible to do
most abortions before 12 weeks and the propagandists will
have far more trouble trying to evoke guilt in women
or moral proscriptions in doctors, religious leaders and
politicians about taking 'medicine', than they are able to
do in the case of surgical abortion – just as the contraceptive pill with its ethos of 'medical science' legitimised birth
control in an earlier period.

Implications of current legislation

The anti-abortion lobby, previously encouraged by the
Tories to mobilise right-wing opinion, seized on the Embryo
Bill as another opportunity to restrict legal abortion. But,
while appearing to support the moralistic stance of the
so-called 'pro-life' groups, even the Thatcher government
had to rule out making abortion completely illegal again.
They could not but recognise the social consequences
of a large scale return to illegal, back-street abortions.
Moreover, considering the swing in public opinion in
support for abortion, they undoubtedly considered it
counter-productive to make themselves unpopular on
what is a secondary issue to them, when they are already
beleaguered by a mass movement against the poll tax
and increased economic difficulties. But the propaganda
machine of the 'pro-life' lobby is not under Tory Party
control.

Even the concession from the government of
guaranteed time to discuss an amendment to the Embryo
Bill has not appeased the anti-choice campaigners.

The Tories have to contend with the fact, moreover, that
public opinion is overwhelmingly against them on a whole
range of 'moral issues', on the health service, privatisation,
the poll tax, etc. The 1988 *British Social Attitudes Survey*
(edited by R Jowell, S Witherspoon and L Brook, *Gower*)
found that public opinion in favour of abortion in all
circumstances increased from 1983-7, with a majority (54

per cent) supporting a woman's right to decide on her own
to have an abortion and 94 per cent supporting abortion in
the case of rape. Even among Catholics, 79 per cent now
favour abortion in the case of rape, 78 per cent when the
woman's health is in danger and 68 per cent (an increase
of 17 per cent in four years) in cases of foetal abnormality.
As in the case of contraception in the past, material interests
win in a battle with religious loyalty.

This is an international phenomenon. In the USA, the
recent attacks on the Roe v Wade amendment to the
Constitution, which in the early 1970s had set a legal
precedent for abortion rights, have led to a series of
attempts to restrict abortion rights in individual states.
However, a massive pro-choice movement has developed.
In Florida and Texas, attempts to restrict rights were
defeated. The House of Representatives, under pressure
from the campaign, voted Federal funds to pay for
abortions for poor women who are the victims of rape
or incest. Bush vetoed this, his stand provoking the now
famous election 'joke' – 'the Republicans are showing real
interest in child welfare – right from conception to deliv-
ery'. But opinion polls show a five to ten point shift in
favour of a woman's right to choose. Although abortion
is considered too controversial an issue in the USA for
Roussel even to apply to do clinical trials on RU 486, the
desperation and poverty of many women in the world's
richest country is such that the US abortion rate in 1988
was 27.4 per 1000 women aged 15-44. This is 50 per cent
higher than Denmark's abortion rate, the highest in western
Europe. Abortion became an election issue in the USA and
victories for the pro-choice candidates underlined the shift
in opinion.

Opposition to these attacks on the right to abortion is a
class and a political issue. We defend the right of everyone
to choose whether or not to proceed with a pregnancy: that
is their own personal, moral or religious decision. What is
not a matter of personal choice, however, is whether our
elected representatives – who owe their position to the
labour movement – are entitled to deny working-class
women the right to make a choice, by denying them
NHS facilities and placing stricter legal restrictions on
abortions. Many Labour MPs who would have preferred
to retain the 28-week limit were compelled to vote tactically
for 24 weeks because a group of 30 to 40 Labour MPs gave

their support to the anti-abortion amendments. It was the voting of these MPs which provided the majority against abortion on demand up to twelve weeks. All Labour MPs should be obliged to follow party policy. If they do not do so and they get a free vote in Parliament, abortion will almost certainly be further restricted in the future. We must campaign urgently for them to follow party policy on this issue.

Abortion is a labour movement issue

The women in the labour movement have been calling for legal abortion ever since the Co-operative Women's Guild passed a resolution in 1934 calling for decriminalisation and an amnesty for those women in prison because they had had, or helped others to have, illegal abortions. Many of the attacks on the Abortion Act, however, resulted in single issue campaigns such as FAB (Fight Alton's Bill), and the Fight the Amendment Campaign. While it is important to draw together as wide a group of women and men as possible to defeat attacks on the 1967 Act, it is also important that the labour movement, and particularly the Labour Women's Organisation, recognise the unique role they must play. The largest ever demonstration for 'a woman's right to choose', the demonstration in 1980 against the Corrie Bill, was called on the initiative of the Women's TUC. The labour movement and the Labour Women's Organisation must campaign under their own name – and for their own demands – as well as working with groups such as FAB, the National Abortion Campaign, or 'Progress' in the case of defending embryo research. It was only in this way that Labour women were successful in mobilising support for birth control in the 1920s and 1930s.

The decline in social conditions compels many women to have abortions. The problems faced by women, particularly working-class women, arise from the general crisis of capitalist society which can offer only a future of poverty, low pay, declining health services and poor housing. They also arise from the unequal and disadvantaged position of women in this society, where they are concentrated in low-paid jobs, suffer high rates of unemployment and still carry the bulk of the responsibility for the care of children, the elderly and sick. In addition to this, their role is constantly belittled and trivialised by the mass media. As long as these conditions exist, there can be no real right to choose: to choose to be childless *or* to choose to have children and be able to bring them up without the poverty and insecurity which can prevent them from reaching their full potential.

Only a socialist programme and the labour movement, men and women, determined to carry it through, can solve the problems women face. We need to inoculate our own movement and the working class against reactionary ideas through political action and campaigns. We must also win to the banner of socialism those women who may become involved in politics for the first time through such issues as abortion or reproductive rights, so strengthening the Labour Women's Organisation and the movement generally.

We are campaigning for:

* A massive injection of funds into the NHS, extension of day-care abortion facilities, and the absorption of private practice, to avoid unnecessary late abortions and to stop profiteering.
* Free abortion on demand: that is, an end to the requirement for two doctors' consent to an abortion; instead, a woman's right to choose.
* Extension of the 1967 Abortion Act to Northern Ireland.
* The democratisation of the NHS to ensure it really reflects the needs of working-class women.
* Good quality, flexible child-care, available for all.
* Child benefits and maternity grants which reflect the real cost of pregnancy and childbirth.
* Maternity and paternity leave for both parents (if applicable) for the first month, followed by a year's parental leave, which may be taken (again, where applicable) by either parent in any combination (for example six months' each; one month on and one month off; or whatever suits them best). This already exists in Sweden.
* A national minimum wage of £150 a week, with *pro-rata* payments for part-timers.

* A 35-hour week with no loss of pay as a step towards the elimination of unemployment.
* Reversal of all Tory cuts and a massive programme of public works to expand housing, education, the NHS, etc.

4. Infertility treatment, Warnock and the new reproductive technologies

What are the new reproductive technologies?

The discovery of the sex hormones led in the 1930s to the production of synthetic hormones which worked in much the same way as natural hormones but could be taken in tablets (not just injected) and were active at relatively low doses. They were first used medically to treat women who did not menstruate properly or who failed to conceive, because their bodies did not produce enough of the natural hormones. The development of chemical knowledge and clinical experience using these hormones enabled the drug industry to use sex hormones for the opposite purpose – contraception – when social attitudes began to change. Hormonal fertility drugs were then introduced in the 1960s. By stimulating ovulation, they enabled many women to conceive who had previously been infertile. But they also led to multiple births, while their side effects could be serious. Information about unwanted effects of these drugs is still not fully available.

Artificial insemination by donor semen (AID) first began to be used as a treatment for infertility in the 1930s. But there was opposition to AID in 1945, and again in the 1950s when a man sued his wife for divorce on the grounds of adultery – because she had used AID without his consent. Revulsion was expressed about a technique adapted from recent use in agriculture but most concern was about 'bastards' inheriting titles and estates, still a matter of major concern to the House of Lords. It shows what their priorities are when it takes 20 pages of Hansard to report their debate on this. The Embryo Act will now prevent children born as a result of donated embryos or sperm from 'inheriting any dignity or title of honour' including the right to use a coat of arms or to occupy the position of hereditary Master of the Household or Banner Bearer, or, of course, the property associated with these titles. Tenants of Glasgow housing schemes will be relieved to know that (according to Lady Saltoun of Abernethy) only the English are divided by class: the Scots are divided by clan instead and can count on the kinship and protection of their clan chief to provide for them.

The Embryo Act will make donor children 'legitimate' if their mothers are married. Their mothers' husbands will be their legal fathers, if the husbands agreed to the treatment. Until now, the 1700 children a year born as a result of AID have been technically illegitimate. However, we would go further and demand that no differentiation should be made between children born in a traditional marriage and those, now 27 per cent of all births, born outside of this arrangement. The Rowntree Report (published on 25 June 1990) forecasts that 50 per cent of children will be born outside marriage in ten years time, while the scientific journal *Nature* (26 October 1989) claims that ten per cent of children have fathers who cannot genetically be the person named on their birth certificate.

The third innovation in the treatment of infertility was *in vitro* fertilisation. The children born as a result of this technique are referred to by the media as 'test tube babies'. *In vitro* fertilisation means fertilisation *in glass* (actually a flat dish, not a test tube). In the normal way, fertilisation takes place in one of a woman's fallopian tubes, which link her ovaries to her uterus. If her fallopian tubes are blocked or damaged, this cannot happen.

The technique of IVF bypasses this problem. First she is given hormone drugs to stimulate the production of eggs. Then the eggs are removed using laparoscopic surgery (a laparoscope is an instrument that allows the surgeon to see inside the woman's body without cutting her open, a bit like the way a periscope lets you see round corners, but on a microscopic scale). They are then fertilised in the dish using her partner's sperm, before being placed back in her uterus. IVF therefore gives a chance to have a child to women with some types of infertility. However, its success rate is low. It involves treatment with drugs whose side effects are not fully understood and it can be a painful process with some risks. Haemorrhaging has happened during egg recovery and three women are reported to have died during surgery.

After ten years of research, and with 80 women having unsuccessful IVF, the first baby born after using the technique was Louise Brown, born in July 1978. There have been 4000 babies born following IVF since then. In 1984, the first baby was born from an embryo which had been frozen and then thawed. There are now between 10,000 and 30,000 frozen embryos in storage throughout the world. In 1987 the first baby was born using a donated egg and IVF; and the first baby was born on the NHS using GIFT (Gamete Intra Fallopian Transfer). GIFT is slightly less high-tech and slightly cheaper than IVF: an egg and some sperm are both placed in a woman's fallopian tube before fertilisation. GIFT is not covered by the Embryo Act.

Surrogacy involves a woman giving birth on behalf of another woman. This can be done using IVF, with the eggs and sperm donated by the couple who will get the baby (the 'social parents') and implanted in the surrogate mother. It can be done using a donated embryo implanted into the surrogate mother or a donated egg and 'social' father's sperm can be implanted into the surrogate mother. Most commonly, it can be done using AID with the sperm donated by the social father. In the last case, the egg is produced in the normal way by the surrogate mother.

The Warnock Report and legislation

The Warnock Report is the report of the Committee of Inquiry into Human Fertilisation and Embryology, chaired by Dame Mary Warnock: *Report of the Committee on Human Fertilisation and Embryology*, (CMND 9314, HMSO, 1984). The White Paper based on the Warnock Report is *Human Fertilisation and Embryology – a Framework for Legislation*, (HMSO, 1987). The Committee was set up in 1982 and reported in 1984. Its task was to examine 'the social, ethical and legal implications of recent and potential developments in human assisted reproduction'.

Enoch Powell introduced a Private Member's Bill in 1984 to try to pre-empt discussion of the issues covered by Warnock and to ban embryo research completely. The Bill fell in 1985. The Tories then introduced the Human Fertilisation and Embryology Bill, or Embryo Bill for short, into Parliament in 1989. Taking note of the campaigns of the right, the government allowed a free vote on embryo research: either the complete banning of research on human embryos that will not be re-implanted in a woman's uterus, or the licensing of laboratories carrying out research on human embryos with a maximum of 14 days' experiments allowed.

Since the publication of the Warnock Report there has been an expansion of clinics offering *in vitro* fertilisation, especially in the private sector. There are now 29 in Britain. A voluntary licensing body already exists. Legislation on surrogate motherhood, one of the issues covered by Warnock, was rushed through in response to the controversy surrounding Kim Cotton, a woman who was paid £6,500 to act as a surrogate mother for a childless couple in 1985.

The legal case of baby M born in the USA as a result of a surrogacy arrangement demonstrates the way in which capitalism distorts personal relationships. William and Elizabeth Stern hired Mary Beth Whitehead to have a child for them in return for $10,000 plus medical expenses. Under the terms of the contract, Mary Beth Whitehead had to undertake all the risks, including that of death. She was to receive no payment if she miscarried in the first five months; she had to agree to an abortion for foetal abnormality if necessary; and also not to drink, smoke or take any medication not prescribed by the Sterns' doctor. In the USA, surrogacy is big business, with the agents receiving $10,000 a time for every surrogate mother they successfully 'market'. In the event, Mary Beth Whitehead changed her mind and wanted to keep the baby. After a lengthy court case, where the main evidence in support of the Sterns was their social status relative to that of Mary Beth Whitehead, the child was taken away and given to the Sterns.

The concept behind surrogacy, that an adult has an overriding right to have a child of 'their own', leads not just to the hiring of a woman's body for nine months, usually the hiring of a working-class woman's body by a wealthy couple, but also to the baby trade. In the last few years, thousands of babies have been stolen, bought or taken under economic or physical duress from their mothers in Latin America and Asia for sale in richer countries. In Britain, commercial surrogacy agencies are already illegal. Private arrangements are allowed but not encouraged and are not enforceable by law. The British Medical Association now supports doctors who act as non-profit making intermediaries in surrogacy arrangements. We are opposed to anyone making a profit out of the desire of some people to have children but recognise that many private arrangements, including arrangements between relatives, will take place anyway. Since these can cause problems for all those concerned, it is vital that counselling services should be provided as part of the NHS.

Warnock was particularly concerned about the ownership, supply and control of eggs, sperm and embryos, and about commercial uses of gene experiments. Frozen embryos will be allowed to be stored for up to five years and their sale will be controlled 'to avoid commercial exploitation'. Whilst we agree with the need for regulation, it also raises the question of *who* decides and *in whose interests*? (Regulation in the interests of working-class people is discussed in Chapters 6 & 7.)

The Warnock Report also spent a lot of time on the legal rights of genetic parents over children, and the rights of children to inherit property. The committee's whole approach reflects traditional conservative ideas about the family, the role of women and motherhood. It deals exclusively with the nuclear family as the environment within which children should be born and brought up, despite the fact that a *Market Research Bureau Survey* in 1988 (*The Guardian*, 26 September 1988) showed that only 3.12 per cent of households fit the stereotyped nuclear family strictly defined as consisting of breadwinning father, dependent mother (with no income of her own) and their children, separate from grandparents, other relatives and friends. It is still only 6.2 per cent of households if you include those where women work part-time. Children are increasingly growing up with single parents, step parents, two parents who are not married to each other, and extended 'families' where the adults may not always be related to one another.

Who is allowed treatment?

To have access to infertility treatment at the present time, it is not enough to have money and patience. You must also conform to the traditional view of motherhood and the family, as reflected in the attitudes of doctors, hospital 'ethical committees' and the Warnock Committee, and soon to be laid down in Codes of Practice under the Embryo Act. This means that only certain women are judged suitable for IVF or artificial insemination, just as some women are judged more 'suitable' than others for injections of Depo-Provera or for NHS abortions. Glasgow, for example, is notorious for the routine administration of Depo-Provera to working-class single mothers living on the housing schemes, with no explanation of the possible side-effects and, in practice, no choice. Social workers in Glasgow have risked disciplinary warnings for objecting to Depo-Provera being administered to their young female clients.

These are not medical but social and moral decisions. Just as women are not allowed to judge for themselves whether they can cope with another pregnancy or need an abortion, they are not allowed either to decide that they want a child so much that the discomfort, pain and, for some people, the humiliation of infertility treatment is worthwhile.

Under the rules adopted by most ethical committees established before the Embryo Act was passed, a woman had to be living in a stable relationship with a man and usually had to be able-bodied. Some clinics were reluctant to treat couples where the man is not in work or the woman not prepared to give up work. Single women and lesbian couples were not usually eligible, although charities like the British Pregnancy Advice Service have been providing AID treatment. In Manchester, a woman was accepted for IVF using these criteria but was later rejected by the medical 'ethical committee' because she had once worked as a prostitute (*The Guardian* 21 October 1987). In another case, a couple arranged to store some of the man's sperm in a sperm bank before he had radiotherapy for cancer as it would sterilise him. The treatment failed and he died but his widow was unable to have artificial insemination or even to get 'custody' of the sperm as she was by then no longer married and in a stable relationship. However, to add insult to injury, she would be allowed to use it if she married someone else.

The Embryo Act contains the following wording: 'A woman shall not be provided with treatment services unless account has been taken of the welfare of any child, including the need of a child for a father, who may be born as a result of the treatment, and of any other child who may be affected by the birth'. Tory MP David Wilshire made it clear in his speech that he was particularly concerned about financial considerations, that 'assisted conception' would not produce families dependent on the state. It was suggested in the debate that the logic of the amendment to include 'the need of a child for a father' (carried by a majority of 52) was that pregnant widows would feel obliged to have abortions.

Brian Liebermann, head of the IVF programme at St Mary's Hospital, Manchester, at a seminar at Manchester University on 9 May 1990, admitted that it was impossible to tell that a 'stable, heterosexual couple' would not split up or repress or abuse their children in the future. On the other hand, he said, he would not be opposed to treating single women or lesbian couples if they convinced him that they would be committed and loving parents. But the ethical committees apply a very narrow and traditional view of who constitute 'good parents', which he implements. The Embryo Act is worded so that IVF or AID treatment is not actually prohibited to single, disabled or unemployed women or lesbians, but conditions under which treatment may be given will be established by Codes of Practice. It is likely that this will formalise what has been general practice in IVF treatment up to now and extend it to AID.

The decisions of health authorities and the courts, when they are involved, invariably reflect an administrative and judicial policy which seeks to promote the traditional role of the family and its ethos. The problems and needs of the individuals concerned are treated as though they were secondary. Yet the traditional model of the family is now markedly at variance with social realities, and conspicuously contradicted by the relationships and households in which a majority of people actually live. Public policy in this field is therefore increasingly arbitrary and bureaucratic. Moreover, while women or couples are denied, in the name of the family, the treatment they need, official reluctance to challenge the sanctity of the family is allowed to hamper effective measures to deal with or even properly investigate problems like child abuse and baby battering which are far from being prevented by the traditional family model. A more realistic approach is now reflected in adoption procedures which allow single people to adopt children.

Single women are often encouraged to adopt or foster girls who have been sexually abused by men, even though the adoption of (scarce) white, able-bodied babies is restricted to the most rigidly stereotyped parents where the man works and the woman guarantees to stay at home with the baby.

Such restrictions on people accepted for IVF could easily be extended to include other political and ideological judgements, for example that black people, working-class people or those who have a criminal record or unconventional life style (which could mean a woman who leaves her children regularly with baby sitters whilst she goes to political meetings or a man who does an unusual amount of housework and childcare) could be discouraged or actually refused treatment. After all, Powell's Bill, which received a lot of Tory votes and 41 out of 85 Labour ones, would have required permission to be given to prospective parents by the Secretary of State. Apart from causing incredible delays, the basis on which people were approved would have been left entirely to the discretion of a minister or more likely his officials.

We are opposed to such social screening of people coming forward for IVF and other treatment. If it were applied to normal conception and childbirth, for example, as a condition for medical care or intervention, it would not be tolerated. Only medical advice – for example, whether IVF or some other treatment is appropriate to the particular problem, the chances of success and the possible side effects – and necessary counselling should be given. The decision to proceed or not should be that of the individuals directly concerned.

Causes of infertility

The priorities of infertility research tell us a lot about the priorities of capitalist society. A great deal of money, research effort by highly qualified doctors and scientists, and media attention, have been devoted to high technology methods (and especially *in vitro* fertilisation) for overcoming or rather by-passing infertility. At the same time, systematic research into the causes of infertility or even the extent of it has been underfunded or not done at all, while NHS facilities and services for infertile people are totally inadequate.

Most estimates suggest that at least one in ten British couples are infertile, although very few systematic surveys have been carried out and reliable information is very limited. The *British Medical Journal* (14 December 1985) reported that as many as one in six couples in one health authority needed help to treat infertility. The Warnock Report recommended that funds be made available for the collection of data on the extent of infertility, its causes, the use of services and the cost to the NHS. The Department of Health has still not made funds available for this. Funds do not even maintain current services. This research would be invaluable but can only be adequately done without affecting the quality of other services by an expansion in real resources for the NHS.

More research must be done into the effects of working conditions and health and safety on fertility. Adverse conditions can also lead to miscarriages and premature labour in women who have no difficulty conceiving. For example, a survey carried out in France showed that women who stood for three hours without a break experienced a 60 per cent increase in premature labour. Women in boring, noisy or wet jobs had double the normal rate of premature labour. Women working with VDUs are also thought to have high rates of pregnancy and birth abnormalities, although this is still being contested.

Chemicals and other materials (for example lead, mercury or vinyl chloride) can cause sterility in both women and men, and we can be exposed to them either in the workplace or as a result of environmental pollution. Radiation also causes infertility in both sexes. Cases of workers suffering from infertility or frequent miscarriage as a result of work in shipyards (near nuclear submarines), in hospital operating theatres (exposed to anaesthetic gases) and in spraying 2,4,5-T weedkiller, for example, have been taken up by unions such as the Agricultural Workers (now TGWU) and the GMB. Out of the 3000 or so chemicals used regularly in manufacturing industry, there are likely to be a considerable number of as yet uncovered causes of infertility and other health risks, threatening particularly the health and well-being of working-class men and women – those most likely to come into contact with them.

Other, mainly avoidable, causes of infertility are contraceptives such as Depo-Provera and IUDs. Pelvic Inflammatory Disease (PID), itself often a side effect of IUDs, is known to be a significant cause of infertility and cases have increased by 50 per cent in the last ten years. A more effective gynaecological service could prevent many cases of infertility from PID, by screening for the bacteria responsible and providing early treatment. Early diagnosis of endometriosis (a condition where misplaced tissue in areas such as the ovary causes pain and malfunction) and research into its treatment would also prevent many cases of infertility as well as relieving the acute pain of the disease.

Stress and a poor diet can be causes or contributory factors in infertility. Working class women work long hours and often suffer stressful conditions both at home and at work. In addition, increasing numbers of women are doing shiftwork which is even more stressful. Protective legislation which restricts the hours a woman may work or the conditions which may be imposed on her is being repealed or undermined by cutbacks in the factory inspectorate and trade union rights.

The manufacturers of drugs, contraceptives and weed-killers and those using chemicals or radioactive materials in their processes, are concerned with making profits. Some of them have been campaigning to weaken health and safety or product safety legislation on the grounds of cost. Some sell products banned for safety reasons in the US or Britain to other countries. None of them is going to bend over backwards to find out about the side effects where the tests are not required by law, because it will cost time and money and a rival might beat them to the commercial launch of a new product.

It is clear why research on high-tech methods of by-passing infertility is more attractive than discovering the causes and taking preventative action. The Tory government and industry, which together provide 90 per cent of funding for research, find the high-tech methods more profitable, while replacing industrial materials or processes would reduce profits.

Many of the major problems confronting those suffering infertility are not addressed by the Human Fertilisation and Embryology Act. It is up to the labour movement to fight all hazards at work and campaign for a safe, healthy environment in which to work and live. Collective action based on the awareness and direct involvement of trade union members is our best protection.

We must campaign for:

* medical services including cancer and other screen-ing on site where appropriate, and available in works' time.
* trade union courses in health and safety for all work-ers in works' time.
* no sacking of women because their working condi-tions are a threat to fertility or pregnancy. Jobs should be made safe for all workers.
* trade unions to take up campaigns for decisive control over health and safety.
* the Health and Safety Executive to be a democratical-ly elected body representing the labour movement and not dominated by management, employers, government representatives and 'experts ' who are more likely to be biased towards the bosses than the workers.
* additional resources for the NHS and public research bodies to extend research and provide better and more widely available treatment for infertility, hand in hand with other improvements in the NHS.

5. Embryo research

What is embryo research?

Embryo research involves fertilised eggs or pre-embryos too small to see with the naked eye. In a normal pregnancy, only a very small proportion of the cells of the pre-embryo will go to form the embryo. The rest will form the placenta and membranes around the embryo. Most pre-embryos will not go on to this stage at all but will fail to implant and be spontaneously aborted. None of these facts, of course, will prevent SPUC from attacking research by referring to 'babies being cut up'.

To judge from the number of times the Warnock Report refers to 'public fears', one of the main aims of the report was to reassure people about the type of research being carried out. It refers to activities which are not and may never be possible (such as producing half-human animals) and which it recommends banning. The hamster test for male fertility, involving the ability of human sperm to penetrate hamster eggs, has been used to whip up fears about 'hybrids'. This test could not possibly produce an embryo or pre-embryo, never mind a human-hamster hybrid. Unfortunately, it refers to these fantastic 'possibilities' in the same breath as discussing IVF and the associated embryo research, which are totally different in character. Clearly, opponents of embryo research will seize on this to draw parallels with 'Nazi-style' experiments, and several speakers mentioned Mengele in the debate in Parliament.

It is essential to opponents of embryo research to confuse the issue in this way. Support for embryo research, where the purpose of such research was understood, stood at 63 per cent in a MARPLAN poll in May 1985. A National Opinion Poll carried out in 1990 found that the proportion of those in favour of research had gone up to 71 per cent. Even SPUC itself found, in its own poll, that a majority supported research!

Why do we support embryo research?

Without embryo research, there would have been no Louise Brown or the thousands that followed her. But before she was born, ten years of experimentation was necessary. That means there have already been twenty years of research, most of it involving human embryos. Only ten per cent of couples receiving IVF treatment succeed in having a child. Further research is necessary to improve this success rate. Banning research could have meant outlawing the examination of embryos for defects before implantation. In opposing research, several 'pro-life' MPs (including Tory Julian Brazier, whose wife was expecting twins as a result of IVF) argued that South Australia had banned research but has still improved its success rate with IVF. The point, of course, is that the results of research done elsewhere are freely available in medical journals.

Embryo research may also identify and prevent spontaneous abortion. At the moment 20 per cent of pregnancies (or 100,000 a year) end in recognised miscarriages. This is the second most common reason, after childbirth, for hospitalisation of women, and causes great distress to women and their families.

Although it is often assumed that problems with infertility are due to some abnormality in the woman, in 40 per cent of couples it is due to the man and in many cases to both partners. Much more research is needed into infertility in both men and women in order both to understand the reasons for it and attempt to cure or by-pass them. Embryo research may also be used to investigate placental tumours.

One of the most important areas of embryo research is in the prevention of inherited diseases. Inherited diseases caused by chromosomal abnormalities or gene defects are suffered by up to 14,000 children a year in Britain. They can be detected by a number of pre-natal tests such as:

Amniocentesis, which can be used to reveal about 80 disorders, not all of which are inherited. A sample of the amniotic fluid surrounding the baby is removed between the 16th and 20th weeks of pregnancy. It then takes three to four weeks to culture the fluid and examine the cells.

Blood screening: the mother's blood can now be tested at 16 weeks' pregnancy for Down's Syndrome, but a positive test needs to be followed up with amniocentesis, as there are often false positive results. This test has only just been introduced. The same sample of blood can be tested for *alpha fetoprotein (AFP)*, a test which has been available for a few years. This will reveal neural tube defects such as spina bifida. It is not yet known whether these are genetic disorders.

Chorionic Villus Sampling (CVS): this is a new technique still in the experimental stage and not widely available, which must be done early in pregnancy, between 8 and 11 weeks. The material examined is from the chorionic villi where the embryo joins the placenta. It contains the same cell material as the embryo and so can be examined for various genetic and chromosomal disorders.

Foetoscopy: this is only available in a few specialist centres. The foetus is actually studied in the womb, with a minute lens in a very fine tube inserted through the abdominal wall. Blood and cell samples can be taken from the foetus and some surgical treatments or a blood transfusion can also be given. These can only be done after 16 to 18 weeks.

Chromosomal abnormalities such as *Down's Syndrome* are only found in humans, so animal experiments cannot be substituted for embryo research in investigating these diseases. Down's Syndrome is caused by an extra chromosome and is not necessarily inherited. It might be caused by exposure to low levels of radiation. If this is the case, it would explain why older women are more at risk: they have been exposed to naturally occurring radiation for longer. At the moment, a pregnant woman might be offered amniocentesis if she is over 35 or has conceived a child with Down's Syndrome before. If she has a positive test result, she then faces the decision about whether to have an abortion. There are 1000 Down's Syndrome children born every year and 50 to 100 aborted. The small proportion is not due so much to the choice of mothers to continue with the pregnancy, as the small number of tests offered. Even in the 'at risk' group, fewer than half are offered the test, partly because of the cost of £100 to the NHS. In Denmark, where screening is widely available, the birth of children with Down's Syndrome has declined rapidly.

The following are examples of diseases caused by gene defects of various kinds:

Duchenne Muscular Dystrophy: a muscle protein is missing causing progressive deterioration of the muscles.

Cystic Fibrosis: mucus clogs up the glands causing problems with digestion and breathing.

Haemophilia: one of the blood clotting factors is missing, causing severe bleeding from what would normally be quite minor injuries.

Sickle Cell Anaemia: an abnormality of the red blood cells which form into solid sickle shapes. Passage of blood through small blood vessels and joints is agonising.

Thalassaemia: similar to sickle cell anaemia, but experienced mostly by people from Indian and Mediterranean (for example Cypriot) families, rather than Afro-Caribbean.

Tay Sachs Disease: a missing enzyme is responsible for this disease which causes blindness, paralysis and dementia. Death by the age of three or four is usual.

Huntingdon's Chorea: in this case the brain is affected, causing personality changes and jerky, uncontrolled movements of the arms, neck and face. This disease does not usually show any symptoms until after the age of 30, when sufferers may have already passed it on to their children.

Epidermolysis Bullosa (EB): a crippling skin disease where the skin and mucous membranes (for example, the lining of the throat and bowel) blister all over. Some children cough up the entire lining of their throats. They usually die young from secondary infections.

Genetic diseases can thus lead to immense suffering, increasing disability and early death. Some can be treated with varying degrees of success and varying degrees of stress for the child and family. Pre-natal screening can eliminate an enormous amount of suffering for carriers of some of the worst genetic diseases.

Pre-natal screening for thalassaemia major, for example, can be done by taking a sample of foetal blood, again at 18 weeks' pregnancy. At University College Hospital in London, where the test is available to women at risk, the number of children born with the disease fell by 78 per cent between 1974/76 and 1980/82. EB can be detected by foetoscopy – a small piece of skin is removed from the foetus and examined with an electron microscope. This cannot be done before the eighteenth week of pregnancy at the earliest and the test itself takes several weeks.

However, the choice of an abortion at four months or more is traumatic for any woman. Chorionic Villus Sampling – where the gene itself is examined earlier in the pregnancy – enables screening to be done for a number of genetic diseases. The test has been made possible by embryo research. It is not yet, however, widely available and the NHS cuts are threatening some of the programmes which are underway.

An alternative to pre-natal screening is *pre-implantation diagnosis*. In this case, IVF techniques are used on women who are not necessarily infertile but are at risk of producing a baby with a genetic or chromosomal disease. The pre-embryo is tested for the disease before being put into the woman's uterus. At the time the Bill was being debated in the House of Lords (in February 1990), this was the subject of embryo research but had not yet been done successfully. In the period between then and the second reading in April 1990, a sex gene probe was developed by Robert Winston at Hammersmith Hospital, and it became possible to replace only female embryos.

This was done, not for the reasons mentioned in the next section, of a cultural preference for one sex over the other, but to avoid genetic diseases only experienced by males, such as *Duchenne muscular dystrophy*. However, because the sex gene probe was the first to be developed, it attracted a lot of publicity precisely on the question of choosing a baby's sex in advance for social rather than therapeutic reasons.

In April 1990, the development of a beta-globin probe was announced for detecting sickle cell anaemia and thalassaemia. Work on Duchenne muscular dystrophy and cystic fibrosis is on-going. Clearly, these tests could not have been developed without embryo research, and embryo research is necessary to develop new tests. These tests could be a major advantage over pre-natal screening. Although it is necessary to go through the procedures of IVF, the alternative for women at risk of giving birth to a child with one of these diseases is to undergo a test during pregnancy, or to take the risk that the baby will not be affected, or not to have children at all. Women who take the test will then have to face the possibility of further choice – whether or not to have an abortion, possibly a late abortion. Many women will choose the physical discomfort of IVF over the emotional and physical distress of a late abortion. This will obviously reduce the need for abortions, particularly late ones. Far from welcoming this possibility, however, SPUC and Life oppose embryo research as well as objecting not just to *late* abortions but to *all* abortions, including those for foetal abnormality.

Opposition to Screening

The 14-day limit for research laid down by the Embryo Act is much better than a complete ban. At the moment, it is an academic question since *in vitro* fertilised eggs start to decay well before the 14-day limit and can no longer be used. However, for the future, it is rather arbitrary and inflexible. In other legislation (for example the Health and Safety at Work Act), it is normal to establish general principles, leaving the numbers (for example, maximum concentrations of toxic materials or time limits for exposure) to be specified in codes of practice. It would be better if the 14-day limit for embryo research were a recommended guide-line for the licensing authority. The Warnock Committee admitted it was arbitrary and were not in agreement about the time limit. In Denmark, the time limit is not specified by law but in a more flexible guideline. The recommended limit is 21, not 14 days. Robert Edwards, the IVF pioneer, suggests 30 days. The Council for Science and Society (*Human Procreation: Ethical Aspects of New Techniques*, Oxford University Press, 1984) recommends a six-week limit since it believes that a foetus can feel no pain before the development, after that period, of a more complex nervous system.

Tests like amniocentesis allow parents to know the sex of their foetus. This has led to pre-natal screening carried out for any reason being attacked because it is open to abuse by parents choosing to have only children of the sex favoured in their culture, usually boys. We are opposed to the abortion of foetuses because they are female, as are the overwhelming majority of medical and nursing staff. The complete eradication of this practice, however, is unlikely to be finally achieved until the inferior status of girls and women is removed. Until then, determined families will always pressure women to abort female foetuses and will find some more acceptable reason for their request for abortion, especially in private clinics where profit is the motive for providing abortions.

There are 3000 conditions which can be inherited, including colour blindness and diabetes, which are either minor defects or can be managed effectively, for example by diet and insulin. Pre-natal screening has also been attacked because it is supposed to open the way to the abortion of any foetus which is less than perfect. This attack implies that women have a callous disregard for children and will undergo abortion for the flimsiest of reasons. There is no evidence for this view, quite the opposite. Women who undergo abortions consider carefully the options open to them. Furthermore, this view is a gross insult in a society where the care of the young, elderly and chronically sick is carried out mainly by women and with very little help from society generally.

Disabled people face a lack of facilities and discrimination throughout their lives. Few firms employ their quota of people with disabilities and when disabled people do get jobs, they are frequently the most monotonous, unsatisfying and badly paid jobs. Similarly, the old and chronically sick are discarded when they are no longer of any use to capitalism, to eke out their lives on a pittance and with those few services achieved in the past increasingly being cut back. We support demands for a massive expansion of facilities for the disabled and those who care for them, so that they can lead as full a life as possible.

Opponents of abortion and of embryo research are fond of quoting examples of families who have found the birth and raising of a disabled child, for example with Down's Syndrome, a rewarding experience. There is no doubt that there are families with the emotional and material resources to cope successfully and who find it a positive experience. It is equally true that many families cannot cope and that some fathers who cannot cope just leave, increasing the chances that mothers of disabled children have to cope with poverty as well as disability and discrimination. In any case, genetic diseases are very different. No one could possibly describe the birth of a child with Tay Sachs disease or EB as a rewarding experience for anyone. It is probably one of the most awful things that could happen.

The lack of facilities and the difficulties which will be encountered by women bringing up disabled children, means *they* must have the right to decide if they can cope. This means the right to choose to continue the pregnancy as well as the right to choose an abortion. At the moment,

75 per cent of UK consultant obstetricians will *only* do an amniocentesis test if the woman agrees in advance that she will have an abortion should it prove positive. This is unacceptable coercion based purely on a profit-and-loss mentality. A positive test and counselling should give a woman and her family a chance to prepare materially and emotionally for the birth of a child with special needs as well as the opportunity for an abortion.

There are grotesque inequalities in the services for people with different hereditary diseases. For example, the Guthrie test for *phenylketonuria* (a metabolic disorder which, if untreated, can lead to mental defects) is widely done on new born babies, who are then treated if necessary. There are 110 specialist centres for haemophilia which offer pre-natal screening and genetic counselling as well as care for those who have the disease. Both are diseases suffered by people of North European origin. There are about 50 born each year, 4000 sufferers in all.

There are a similar number of people who suffer from sickle cell anaemia and thalassaemia, and the birthrate of people with these two diseases is three times that of those with haemophilia. These diseases predominantly affect people from an Afro-Caribbean and Mediterranean background respectively. The Department of Health provides no money to help them, describing the diseases as 'exotic' and 'rare'. There is a pre-natal test for Muscular Dystrophy too, but the Department of Health will not pay for it and so the Muscular Dystrophy Group must raise the necessary £200,000 a year by organising raffles, jumble sales and coffee mornings. DEBRA, the EB association, has also had to raise money for research into the disease, treatment and pre-natal screening. It is shameful that essential care and research is funded by charity, while tax cuts are given to the rich and public expenditure is squandered on weapons and in selling off public assets.

Research must be backed up by resources to allow proper screening to take place, counselling for those then found to be carriers of an inherited disease or pregnant with an affected foetus, and assistance to those born with such diseases. To provide these, a massive expansion of the welfare state is needed, as well as a full range of other services to ensure the health and well-being of working-class people.

Consequences of banning embryo research

The consequences of banning embryo research and therefore, in effect, assigning legal rights to the embryo, would have also provided a stronger basis for the opponents of abortion to make further attacks on the 1967 Abortion Act.

Assigning the embryo legal rights could also have provided a stronger basis for restrictions on the rights of pregnant women in favour of rights attributed to the foetus. Mothers could more easily have been sued by others on behalf of their children for pre-natal negligence or, if things went wrong, for having home births. Although the general trend in opinion is currently going against this type of legal action, the campaigns of Life and SPUC, even where the legal changes they support are defeated, are used to try to swing public opinion against the rights of women. Pregnant women have been subjected to major surgery and other treatment without their consent. For example, several American women have been served with court orders requiring them to have caesarean sections because their doctors judged it necessary but the women had refused to give their consent. One woman in Michigan and another in Colorado had already had normal deliveries before the court orders arrived! In 1981 a Los Angeles juvenile court 'took jurisdiction' over a foetus, thereby confining its mother to hospital for the last two months of pregnancy. A court of appeal overturned the ruling but by then she had already given birth.

These extreme cases from the USA rest on a traditional view, upheld by sections of the judiciary but increasingly under challenge and discounted by many sections of society, that the main role of women is as 'breeders'.

6. Infertility and private medicine

Infertility treatment and the National Health Service

Like many NHS services, infertility treatment is under-funded. A survey by Frank Dobson MP showed that infertility services are better in the South of England than in the North, Midlands or Wales, but that even in the South 40 per cent of District Health Authorities have little or no provision for infertility treatment. It is possible to wait longer than 30 weeks for a first clinic visit and four years for treatment. Fewer than half the authorities do ovarian scanning, microsurgery or radio immune assay tests of hormone levels, and only one in five does all three, even though these facilities are essential for an effective infertility service.

In the whole of Britain only the IVF treatment at St Mary's Hospital in Manchester and the University of Wales, Cardiff, are funded entirely by the NHS and provided free to all patients. However, in the case of St Mary's only people from the North West are eligible for treatment, and patients can wait for up to four years for their first appointment.

The purely physical side of infertility treatment available on the NHS is limited enough, but facilities to deal with the patients' thoughts and feelings are even worse. Very little counselling is available, and even the opportunity for patients to discuss their cases and alternative options for treatment is limited. Fewer than one in four health authorities provide either. Distress caused by providing infertility treatment in the same clinics or departments as birth control, abortion or even ante-natal care is all too common.

The lack of information or counselling and the concentration on the mechanics of the problem is not limited to infertility treatment, but is widespread in medical practice, especially in relation to women's health. Pre-menstrual tension (PMT) has only recently been recognised as a serious problem by some doctors, as have the problems caused by the menopause. Women are often treated as if their genuine health concerns are trivial and even imaginary. Examinations can be carried out with a great deal of insensitivity, as though discomfort or indignity are just things women must put up with. Even when life-threatening diseases like breast cancer are diagnosed, it is unusual for the bad news to be broken in the most sensitive way possible (with a friend present, for example).

Unfortunately, it is far from being normal for the patient to be treated, not as just a collection of malfunctioning components, but as a whole person with intelligence and emotions, and the ability to make choices about her treatment. Such an approach is essential if the patient is going to be able to contribute actively to her own recovery, which can be a vital factor for survival. There are many doctors, nurses and other staff who strive to understand the different needs of their patients. But the treatment of women by the medical profession and the health-care system in general reflects the dismissive attitudes prevalent in a society which discriminates against women.

It was to overcome this approach to women's health care that led to the campaigns for Well Women's Clinics, and to their successful establishment first in the Manchester area and later elsewhere. But there still needs to be an expansion of the Well Women's Clinic network and changes within the NHS to ensure that health-care services are sympathetic and sensitive to the needs of patients. This means proper training not only in medical care itself, but in relating to patients (and their families and close friends where appropriate). This in turn requires good staffing levels and additional resources. There is a general need for the expansion and improvement of NHS services, not just IVF and other infertility treatments.

Infertility treatment and private practice

Apart from St Mary's and the University of Wales, the few clinics which provide IVF free on the NHS also provide a private service. There are currently 42 centres offering IVF, of which 36 also offer GIFT. Another 17 are about to be set up. There were 43 centres in 1989 just offering GIFT. Infertility treatment has become big business, with IVF particularly profitable. Margaret Brazier, law lecturer at Manchester University, commented 'reproductive medicine is a thriving business that will benefit from the Bill's enactment' (*New Statesman*, 20 April 1990). It has been one of the major areas of expansion of private practice. IVF costs a minimum of £2,000 to £3,000, plus travel and hotel costs. The success rate is quite low, about 10 per cent. If it does not work the first time, then the process has to be repeated.

This sort of money is obviously beyond the means of most working-class women, although one clinic in Sheffield offers the treatment for £600. The cost is likely to increase once the new licensing authority is in operation, which is intended to be from Summer 1991. It will cost an estimated £500,000 just to establish the authority, excluding running costs, but the government has allocated no funds to pay for this, so the cost will be passed on to the centres in the form of licensing fees, and in turn on to the patients. Nevertheless, despite the massive costs, in their desperation to have children, couples will take out bank loans or second mortgages and run up enormous debts to obtain treatment. Moreover, in the private sector especially, it cannot be assumed that the best interests of the patient and the clinic which operates for profit are entirely compatible. For example, a young woman in a recent television documentary was given £1,500 worth of tubal surgery when her partner had not even had a £2 sperm count.

The very poor provision of infertility treatment on the NHS, and the existence of enough couples in a position to find up to £3,000, contributes to this expansion of the private sector. Patrick Steptoe, who pioneered IVF, was a consultant gynaecologist at Oldham General Hospital. He worked there for years without being able to get funds from the NHS or Medical Research Council. He then established a private clinic with his colleague, Robert Edwards, at Bourn Hall near Cambridge.

A major expansion of resources for the NHS is needed so that these and many other services can be available to all, not just to those who can pay. We must campaign for these resources, for research on all aspects of fertility and infertility, and for facilities for treatment on the NHS. Even Edwina Currie, staunch supporter of Thatcher and the private sector, said in the Embryo Bill debate that research (if not treatment) should be done by the NHS, so that it could be controlled, so that it would benefit everyone, and so that it could not be exploited by the unscrupulous.

The medical profession and the control of research

Shortage of NHS funds for infertility treatment is not the only reason for the development of private medicine and the concentration on high-tech methods. Professional interests also play a part. The hierarchical establishment which dominates the medical profession has a great deal of power and influence, and will go to great lengths to protect what it sees as the profession's interests. Nye Bevan and the 1945 Labour government discovered this when the NHS was being set up. The leaders of the profession and a large section of its ranks have a long history of conservatism, with both a small and a large 'C', opposing radical ideas in medical practice as well as in politics. Pasteur's theory that disease was transmitted by bacteria was strenuously opposed. Pasteur, after all, was a mere scientist, not a doctor. Doctors opposed birth control and abortion for many years, and when they could no longer prevent the widespread use of contraception or the legalisation of abortion, they tried to assert their own control in these fields by insisting that first contraception, and later abortion, should only be available for strictly medical reasons.

Doctors and scientists may be influenced by a variety of motives. The best are undoubtedly motivated by concern for their patients and a desire to advance medical science. Doctors and researchers, however, do not work in a social vacuum. Their selection, education, training, and career advancement reflect the system of society in which we live. Specialisation, which is sometimes taken to extreme lengths, and the compartmentalisation of research and treatment (with separate administrative bodies and career ladders, and often competition for scarce funding) generates a narrowness of approach which often prevents researchers from seeing their work in a wider context.

In capitalist society, moreover, doctors and scientists are far from being immune from material pressures. Scientific and clinical questions are invariably bound up with various career interests, which means salaries, promotion, professional recognition, status, and prestige. Research which is dramatic, exciting and technically complex – like IVF – attracts more scientists and doctors than the more mundane projects which may have a higher chance of success. Similarly, an application for a research grant for a more prestigious line of research which has to be recommended by other researchers doing similar work is more likely to be successful.

Doctors and scientists tend to assert their professional authority to lay down public policy on issues like embryo research on the grounds that only they have the necessary knowledge and experience to take such decisions. Clearly, we rely on medical and scientific professionals to advance medical knowledge and develop new treatments. While professionals play a vital role, however, other sections of society, particularly working-class people who make up the overwhelming majority of NHS patients, must also have a say in assessing new technology and checking the availability and quality of treatment.

Warnock and organisations like Progress (which is campaigning against the criminalisation of embryo research) argue that the doctors and scientists can best represent the public's interest in this field. They support the professional experts against the 'non-scientific', 'political' or 'moral' objections of the groups opposing embryo and related research. The positions of different sections of the medical profession, however, is far from being determined by purely 'scientific' considerations. Doctors' views and decisions are also influenced by traditional ideas and prejudices. The religious views of some consultants, for instance, lead to marked regional differences in the availability of NHS abortions. In the West Midlands, only 21 per cent of abortions are done on the NHS, while the proportion is as high as 88 per cent in some other regions.

The privileged social background from which most doctors are still selected, combined with the elitist ethos of the profession, means that most doctors are separated by a wide gulf in outlook and experience from the majority of their patients. All too many doctors simply do not accept the need to make their diagnosis and proposed treatment comprehensible to their patients. Many, though perhaps well intentioned, are unable to communicate in a way that enables patients to understand and come to terms with the health problem, or complex of problems, that they are experiencing. In some cases, the gap in social attitudes is aggravated by blatant prejudice against working-class people in general, and especially towards women.

Doctors frequently make decisions without fully communicating with their patients, and certainly without acknowledging the validity of patients' own views and feelings. In a survey by Wendy Farrant (H Homans, *The Sexual Politics of Reproduction*, edited by L Flomax, Gower Press 1985), 25 per cent of consultants thought it unnecessary to obtain the woman's consent to alpha feto protein (AFP) screening for spina bifida. The fact that some doctors, such as Wendy Savage for example, work only for the NHS, communicate with their patients and respect their wishes, does not alter the general rule. On the contrary, the attack on Wendy Savage by the medical hierarchy only underlines the fact that doctors like her are exceptional. However, some views are changing. A recent survey showed that 73 per cent of gynaecologists agreed women should have the right to decide whether or not to have an abortion after medical consultation (Hansard, 14 December 1989).

Mary Warnock, in a lecture at Cambridge University's Department of History and Philosophy of Science in 1986, referred to women's 'appalling fear and ignorance about science'. But women are wary of medical and technological innovations through experience, not fear and ignorance. Women are aware of the tragedies caused by the prescription of Thalidomide to pregnant women in the early 1960s, or the routine use of X-rays in the 1950s to study foetal development, and wider experience of innovations at work, like automation, word processing or manufacturing processes which use dangerous chemicals. The use of science to develop ever more destructive weapons, and recent publicity about environmental pollution, also makes them regard science as potentially hostile to their interests. Even the current balance of embryo research projects is an indication that factors other than the need to improve the quality of life are involved. Of 53 current projects, six are studying the prevention of genetic defects, one is about research into a contraceptive vaccine, and the other 46 are for improvements in IVF techniques, the area with the most prospect in the short term for generating profitable discoveries.

Licensing under the Act

The main part of the Human Fertilisation and Embryology Act brings under state control the treatment of infertility by *in vitro* fertilisation and artificial insemination, including treatment using donated sperm, eggs or embryos; the storage of donated or 'spare' sperm, eggs and embryos; and research involving human embryos. To do this, a statutory Independent Licensing Authority will be set up to issue licenses to clinics and laboratories carrying out any of these activities. At the moment, this is done by a Voluntary Licensing Authority, set up by the Medical Research Council along lines recommended by the Warnock Report and chaired by Dame Mary Donaldson. The Act has specified various conditions for the granting of licenses, and Codes of Practice will spell them out in more detail.

For a clinic to get a licence to provide IVF, the person in charge will have to be approved; back-up facilities (for example, a hospital) will have to be available for emergencies; and the training, qualifications and numbers of staff (including counsellors) will have to be approved. The licensing authority will specify what sort of consent form patients will have to sign; what records will have to be kept; how confidentiality will be protected; the maximum number of pre-embryos to be implanted; and will have to approve the ethical guidelines about who is approved for treatment. The Act has specified that donors will be anonymous. There will be no right given to donor children when they become 18 to find out who the donor was. However, the information will be made available 'in exceptional circumstances', for example, if the child were to sue British Nuclear Fuels for being damaged as a result of damage done to its biological father, in the case of a donor who might have worked at Sellafield. This has implications for the records that are kept, and who has access to them, and thus to agreements made between the clinic and licensing authority on these matters.

To get a licence to do embryo research, the main consideration is likely to be the nature and purpose of the research and whether the same information could have been obtained without using human embryos. Opponents of research, in a last ditch stand after Parliament had voted to allow it, unsuccessfully attempted to restrict the purposes for which research could be done, for example, by trying to exclude research aimed at improving contraceptive technology.

Members of the new authority will be appointed by the Secretary of State. At least a third but fewer than half of the members will be doctors or people working with human embryos, sperm or eggs (though the rest could still be other research scientists). These proposals are inadequate, mainly because the authority is controlled only by the Secretary of State and because it is made up of 'experts', some of whom will be doctors and scientists financed by private companies, 'policing' other 'experts'. Attempts were made to add religious representatives to the list of 'experts', but the amendment was lost by 31 votes.

Drugs, including contraceptives, are already controlled by a similar body. New drugs are licensed by the medicines division of the Department of Health on the advice of the Committee on the Safety of Medicines (CSM). We do not deny that these experts know a lot about pharmaceuticals, but they do not necessarily act in our interests, and often defend the pharmaceutical industry at our expense. They are very close to the industry being regulated, not only because they are all professionals who have studied together, meet at conferences, play golf, join gentlemen's clubs and so on, but because the whole process of licensing relies on close and friendly co-operation. An Open University television film of the drug licensing process showed the licensers asking the manufacturers' advice about what tests they should recommend. The first Chair of the then voluntary Drug Safety Committee, Derrick Dunlop, was offered and accepted a directorship of Sterling Pharmaceutical Co., at the end of his term of office.

More recently, John Griffin, Head of the Medicines Division 'went over to the enemy', as the *New Scientist* put it (14 February 1985), to become the Director of the Association of the British Pharmaceutical Industry (ABPI), the manufacturers' organisation. Earlier, the *New Scientist* (17 March 1983) had said, 'The CSM did little better with Practolol . . . than was done without legislation in the case of

Thalidomide'. Practolol was withdrawn by ICI as a result of serious side effects. The same article concluded that Opren was withdrawn in 1982 only after considerable delay, for two reasons. The first was 'the deplorable secrecy which surrounds the whole business of drug regulation'. The second was that 'such a cosy relationship' between the regulators and the industry 'cannot stand the strain of a disaster and leads to complete paralysis of action in the resultant crisis'. We do not want this 'cosy relationship' to continue in drug licensing, or to be the model for the Human Fertilisation and Embryology Authority. Chapter 7 describes our alternative for the control of embryo research and pharmaceuticals in the interests of working-class people, together with our demands for a range of fertility and infertility treatments accessible to all.

7. For democratic control of research and health care

If contraception, abortion and infertility treatment are to be available to all those who want them, they must be provided free by the National Health Service. That, in turn, means that the labour movement must confront two major obstacles: private ownership and the lack of democratic control of both the pharmaceutical industry and the NHS itself.

Private ownership

Private ownership of the pharmaceutical industry, private medical practice and private firms supplying scientific and medical instruments, diagnostic testing kits, artificial limbs and other equipment for the disabled, are all a burden on the NHS. Under the Tory government, privatisation of services such as catering and cleaning have led to a further deterioration in the NHS, as well as in the wages and conditions of its workers. The NHS, or individual patients, have to pay for the profits of the private firms, on top of the goods and services themselves. Moreover, provision primarily for profit rather than need distorts the range of goods and services available.

For example, private medical insurance, and even private medical practice itself, is often restricted to more routine treatments. For complex treatment, requiring high levels of skill or newly developed techniques, patients may often be referred to the NHS. The case of infertility treatment is slightly different in that high tech methods like IVF are the more profitable ones. But here, too, years of experimental work was done in the public sector before successful and therefore potentially profitable techniques were discovered. Private medical insurance still does not cover the treatment. Where NHS consultants and clinics also provide the treatment privately, there is a lot of pressure to 'go private'. Waiting lists for treatment, built up as a result of lack of NHS resources, may be exploited to push people into paying for private treatment.

The profit motive means that the drug industry allocates few resources to developing drugs for rare or tropical diseases (as the potential market is either too small or too poor to be very profitable) compared to new varieties of existing drugs (where the market is more certain and the amount of new scientific and technological knowledge required is less). It also means companies are less likely to do research which is risky, because, for instance, the disease is not well understood. Firms will also be reluctant to finance research into diseases related to diet or unsafe working conditions, where the chances are slim of producing a chemical that will, by itself, cure the disease and thus become a profitable commodity.

In the area of fertility control, the potential market for contraceptives, abortion pills or fertility drugs is fairly certain and the research is relatively straightforward, so the profit motive is not likely to divert research *away* from this general area. However, *within* this field the search for profits is an obstacle to the development of a product that best meets the needs of men and women and is safe.

First of all, companies do not generally ask potential patients what they want or whether symptoms like headaches or nausea, for example, really are just the trivial side-effects research scientists and doctors say they are. (In fact, they must think women will put up with almost anything, because development of a contraceptive drug for men was abandoned because it had just these effects.) This is not just an effect of the profit motive and the cost of finding out what men and women really want; it is another consequence of the attitude that scientists and doctors know best and do not need to consult their patients (as discussed in Chapter 6).

Secondly, in the case of contraceptives especially, drugs taken by healthy women (or men) over long periods of time need to be much safer than drugs taken to cure diseases over short periods or where the disease is much worse than any unwanted side-effects of the drug. Drug companies do the tests they are required to do and no more. They do not look for extra work, expense or delay in launching new drugs. Long-term effects may only show up when large numbers of people have taken them over a period of time, not under clinical conditions, but under normal conditions, without the kind of monitoring by doctors which takes place in trials.

The existence of private practice undermines the original concept of the NHS, that no matter what your income or where you live, you should have equal access to treatment. However, the compromise made in 1948, which allowed the continuation of private practice, meant that a two-tier system based on ability to pay developed. The private sector also causes a steady haemorrhaging of staff and resources from the NHS. In the last twenty years, cuts in the NHS have encouraged private practice and insurance. This has been deliberately fostered by Thatcher since 1979.

Private medical practice should be ended, to remove profit from medical treatment, integrate the resources of the current private sector into the NHS, and complete the process begun in 1948. No one but those who stand to lose their fat fees (and extreme monetarist economists) would attempt to defend making money out of ill health once the NHS was revitalised. Most doctors are fully committed to a national health service, and many consultants who make money out of private practice would not see the need to do so if they got the necessary resources for research and treatment within the NHS.

The record of the privately owned drug companies was examined in a previous chapter. In 1988 the NHS bill for prescription drugs was £2.7 billion, or 10 per cent of total NHS spending. Through their often irresponsible marketing of drugs, their control of innovation in drug treatment, and their massive profits, which impoverish the NHS, the drug companies have themselves demonstrated the need to end private control.

The pharmaceutical industry should be brought under public ownership. This must be based on socialist national-isation, not the bureaucratic state ownership of the past. Previous Labour governments nationalised public utilities (like water, the railways, gas and electricity) and old heavy industries (like coal, steel, ship-building, and parts of the car industry) with massive compensation to former owners who had presided over the decline and, in some cases, almost complete ruin of these sectors. In many cases, sections of big business willingly accepted nationalisation of these essential but frequently loss-making industries, though they always feared the precedent set by a section of private owners being made redundant.

Labour governments, however, invariably appointed merchant bankers, industrialists and former owners to run public corporations primarily to serve the need of the private sector for cheap energy, industrial goods and services. In spite of this, the pressure of the labour movement ensured that the wages and conditions (particularly, for example, health and safety in the mines) were improved in the nationalised industries, another cause of capitalist hostility to public ownership. But there was no element of workers' democracy.

The completely non-socialist character of the nationalised sector enabled the Tories to discredit it as an inefficient, bureaucratic caricature of 'socialism'. The leadership of the labour movement, moreover, completely failed to defend the positive gains of nationalisation, particularly of the measures carried through by the 1945 Labour government. Since 1979 the Thatcher government, capitalising on the massive assets built up over decades of state investment, has handed large sections of the nationalised industries back to big business at knock-down prices. A combination of asset-stripping, cut-backs in capacity and the work-force, and new technology has made them highly profitable. It is predictable, however, that in the hands of investors motivated by short-term profitability, many of these industries will again be starved of the investment they need to meet the real needs of society.

Socialist nationalisation, or genuine social ownership, would bring the resources of the pharmaceutical industry, built up by the efforts of its work-force and on the profits made out of ordinary people, under the control of working-class people through their elected representatives. The industry's resources could be used to develop a drug production and research sector as an integral part of the NHS. This would be one step in financing the very necessary rebuilding and expansion of the NHS. It would go hand in hand with the payment of decent wages to nursing, ancillary staff, ambulance and other workers, as well as much shorter hours for junior doctors and resources for all areas of research and treatment.

Democratic workers' control and management.

At present, industry and finance are in the hands of a wealthy minority who owe their position overwhelmingly to inherited wealth and privilege. The wealthiest one per cent of people in Britain (around 400,000 people) own twenty per cent of marketable wealth (property, shares, bank deposits, etc., excluding pension rights); while the wealthiest ten per cent own 54 per cent. This wealthy elite constitutes a ruling class which not only owns and controls the commanding heights of the economy (in which the 200 biggest companies control 90 per cent of capital assets), but also has a decisive influence over the state and the administration of society generally. Although a public service, the NHS is run by a bureaucratic management who operate within the framework of capitalist interests. Until the NHS is run by democratic bodies which represent the interests of the working class, the health service will never be able to meet adequately the needs of workers and their families.

It is therefore vital that the NHS and related industries like pharmaceuticals are run as publicly owned bodies under workers' control and management. This would mean over-all management of the health service nationally and regionally by bodies dominated by the elected represent-atives of the NHS trade unions, patients, community groups and the labour movement as a whole. All representatives should be subject to recall, to ensure accountability, and receive no more than the wages of skilled workers, to ensure they do not become remote from the people they are representing. At the same time, there should be day-to-day workers' control of each work-place exercised by the elected trade union representatives of NHS workers, to defend the wages, health and safety, and general conditions of the NHS workers and to provide an additional check on management bodies.

Democratic management bodies would run the health service in the interests of working-class people, allocating resources and deciding priorities for preventative medi-cine, treatment, and research. Naturally, these democrat-ic bodies would draw fully on the expertise of doctors, scientists, and other technical specialists (who would also be represented through their trade unions). In a society based on planned production to meet individual and social needs rather than profit, there would be no fundamental conflict of interests between doctors, scientists and trade unionists.

Chapter 6 examined the way in which doctors' and scientists' interests could diverge from those of the women seeking treatment. The doctors and scientists who are at the moment in charge of research programmes and clinical departments are the consultant gynaecologists and obstetricians, and professors of physiology, embryology and molecular biology. The vast majority of scientific and technical work, however, is done by junior doctors, technicians, research assistants, spectroscopists, statisticians, computer programmers and other workers. Without them, research would be impossible, yet they are rarely recognised publicly as doing much of the work. They are often members of the Manufacturing, Science and Finance Union and other NHS unions. They may well have different views about control of research from that of consultants, and would certainly take part in elections of representatives to committees controlling the priorities for and the direction of research.

The right to choose

It is only through the extension of democratic public ownership in the field of health services that women will achieve the right to choose in relation to reproductive technology and health care generally. Women are no longer prepared to accept paternalistic treatment from consultants and administrators, but are increasingly demanding the right to take their own decisions.

* All decisions about treatment must ultimately be taken by the woman to be treated. Socialists must campaign for the widest possible range of facilities to be made available to enable the fullest possible choice to women. The role of doctors in this should be to offer their advice on which methods are appropriate in each case, what is entailed in each, the chance of success and the possible side-effects. Social and 'ethical' decisions about the suitability of the individual to be treated based on class, race or life-style are unacceptable.

*   Patients must be allowed access to their medical records. Information about our health and treatment should not be kept from us on the grounds that we might not be able to cope with the knowledge, or for so-called 'ethical reasons' or 'reasons of confidentiality' (what reasons?). Patients must be recognised as being as much a part of the 'team' dealing with their own health-care as the surgeons, physicians, nurses, physiotherapists, counsellors and other medical and paramedical workers. By making treatment our decision and having the right to information about our own health, we will develop the confidence to question doctors, learn more about our own bodies, and gain more control over our lives.

Conclusion: prospects and policies

Advances in scientific knowledge and new technology have created the potential for women to have much more control over their own fertility than in the past. Since bearing and raising children still determines the pattern of most women's lives, it is clear that women's control of their fertility is vital if they are to control their own lives.

Socialists support 'a woman's right to choose'. We support measures which protect the health and well-being of working-class people, and which improve the morale of young people, not forcing on them decisions for which they feel unready. We believe that past reforms, such as the provision of birth control, have been an important factor in improving women's health and have encouraged the involvement of the present generation of women in the labour movement and in community campaigns to improve their position in society.

However, as we have shown in this book, 'a woman's right to chose' is not just a matter of an individual's personal choice, but is constrained by material circumstances such as poverty or the condition of the NHS. It is in large measure determined by those in our society who have the power to make decisions: for example, the medical establishment. Finally, it is strongly influenced by the ideology of the particular society in which we live, including traditional views of women's role and of the family.

A growing rejection of Tory ideology

Ideological obstacles to women's choice work by inducing feelings of guilt in many women who have abortions and by generating a sense of failure in women who are unable to have children 'of their own'. This sense of failure is one which men are also conditioned to feel very strongly.

The Tories have attempted to reinforce reactionary ideology about women to create a climate of opinion in which the consequences of their anti-working class policies, such as cuts in the NHS and in local authority services catering for the young, disabled and elderly, are accepted or at least tolerated. They present these services as being best performed 'in the community', which means, in practice, by women in their own homes and without pay.

They also use such ideology to give the impression that the social problems caused by capitalism in a period of decline are the fault of individual men and women ('absent fathers' and 'working mothers'). The idea is to avert the finger of blame from the real culprits: those who own and control society – the bosses, the Tory Party and their friends.

However, it is increasingly clear that the Tory Party, by and large, has failed to gain widespread acceptance for such ideas. On the contrary, surveys show that public opinion is moving away from the most reactionary ideas, and reflects more realistically how people actually live.

The most significant factor in bringing about this shift of opinion has been the large number of women joining the work-force. Women are now 45 per cent of the work-force. The UK Labour Resources Survey predicts that this will rise to 50 per cent by the year 2000, with approximately 83,000 extra female workers each year (*The Independent* 1 October 1990).

According to the *Family Change and Future Policy* report published by the Family Policies Study Centre, 30 per cent of mothers with children under three work: 11 per cent full-time and 19 per cent part-time. Forty-six per cent of mothers of 3- to 4-year-olds work: 11 per cent full-time and 35 per cent part-time. It is little wonder, considering the enormous contribution of women and their numbers in the work-force, that traditional tenets, such as 'a woman's place is in the home', fly in the face of reality and are therefore being increasingly rejected by large sections of the population. It is also not surprising that those age groups most involved at the moment in raising children, and the women in those age groups in particular, should be the ones to have changed their views most markedly.

In an *Independent*/Newsnight survey (*The Independent* 21 September 1990), fewer than one-third of the people interviewed held traditional views of the family, that is that mothers should stay at home and look after young children. Particularly radical views were held by under-35s. The majority thought that it was reasonable for both parents to work and that fathers were as suitable as mothers to look after under-5s, even though a majority might not put these views into practice.

Women surveyed had less traditional views than men, including views on subjects where reactionary ideas have been most tenacious. For example, 32 per cent of under-35s thought that homosexual couples should be allowed to adopt children. But among women under-35, 42 per cent thought that lesbian couples should be allowed to adopt, and 35 per cent thought that gay male couples should be allowed to do so.

The Tories have been forced to recognise such changes. For example, their response to the amendments attacking abortion rights, when the Warnock legislation was being discussed in parliament, was more neutral than before. They have also tried to harness the mood of women for their own purposes, by condemning rape and domestic violence and calling on the police to take these issues seriously. Of course, this is pure hypocrisy on their part. The cuts in transport and in finances for battered women's refuges, and the changes in social security and housing benefits, along with the poll tax and cuts in local authority provision across the board, mean that there will be less practical means to help prevent rape and domestic violence, and to help women escape violent relationships or support them in the aftermath of such violence.

Moreover, the Tories still try hard to trade on backward ideas that have been less decisively undermined, such as prejudice against gays and lesbians. The Warnock legislation restricts infertility treatment to heterosexual couples in stable relationships. We are opposed to the availability of treatment being subject to criteria of 'eligibility', whether decided by the medical hierarchy or the government. In reality, the imposition of such criteria means that every prospective candidate for treatment is subjected to an ideological/political test. Treatment should be accessible to all who want it, based only on the medical indications that the treatment sought is appropriate to the conditions.

The majority of women are challenging traditional views of themselves. They will inevitably be forced to consider what are the material consequences of such views.

They will want more control over reproduction, but their demands will inevitably go far beyond that. Despite going out to work, full-time women workers still carry out 87 per cent of the approximately 50 hours a week involved in child-care. It is inevitable that they will demand more facilities to be provided in the community as well as more sharing of responsibility in the home.

The sharpening battle for resources

Although the ideological grip of Tory tradition has been loosened, there still remains an enormous battle to be fought for resources. Socialists stand for the right of women to choose to have a child and raise it without the poverty, bad housing conditions, and the lack of good education and health facilities which restrict the lives and potential of women and children at present.

For those who require infertility treatment to have children, the question inevitably arises: where can you get treatment, and where will the money come from? The Warnock legislation dealt purely with regulating the conditions under which treatment is provided, not with resources to make the treatment more widely available – even to those deemed 'eligible'.

Undoubtedly, women have suffered most from cuts in the health service. According to the London Health Emergency Group, apart from cuts in areas of health care that affect everyone, there has been a 'significant erosion in the family planning, gynaecology and abortion services and inadequate progress on screening services for cervical and breast cancer . . . (together with) the closure of local maternity hospitals' (*Daily Telegraph* 23 May 1990).

West Lambeth Health Authority, which performs the highest number of abortions in the country, has cut the number of NHS abortions to be carried out weekly from 35 to 9. This is to save £150,000. They have contracted out their service to a private clinic charging £220 per abortion. A local doctor commented that this would inevitably mean a rise in the number of unwanted children, women going into debt to pay for abortions and an increase in the number of self-induced abortions (*South London Press* 12 October 1990).

We are now facing a general crisis in the NHS caused by over a decade of cuts, further aggravated by the government's determination to push through its latest round of 'reforms' based on the introduction of a so-called 'market culture', and centring around the 'opting-out' of hospitals. The government's edict that hospitals must balance their books by the beginning of the next financial year in April 1990, has sharply increased the number of ward closures, resulting in massive waiting lists. Even emergency patients are being made to queue for beds. Consultants in some areas take decisions on whether or not to perform life-saving treatment on the basis of an unofficial point system.

Cuts in health care, moreover, have been accompanied by cutbacks in medical research. As a result of the government's squeeze of its funds, the Medical Council is currently £3 million 'over budget' and it has recently decided to close down several projects: a cryobiology unit at Cambridge studying techniques for freezing tissue in transplant surgery; Glasgow's blood pressure unit; and the recently established Cambridge molecular neurobiology unit (*The Observer* 19 August 1990). Medical research is suffering the same fate as civil (i.e. non-military) research and development as a whole, which is falling further and further behind the rest of Europe and Japan, especially as increased numbers of scientists leave for better facilities and prospects abroad. The Science and Engineering Research Council has been able to fund only 60 per cent of its alpha-rated research grant applications 1988-90 (*New Scientist* 22 September 1990), while the Medical Research Council is unable to fund 300 of the projects it approves every year.

It is not only NHS cuts which restrict the real choices available to women. The current destabilisation of the NHS comes after a decade when, in relation to health, the gaps between wealthy and poor have been steadily widening. Social class differences in mortality rates have widened since the Black Report, which focussed attention on them, was virtually suppressed by the government ten years ago. The latest study, published in the *British Medical Journal* by Dr David Smith and others, comments: 'Studies of differential mortality . . . reiterate the fact that British society is stratified to a fine grain from top to bottom' (*The Guardian* 17 August 1990).

The availability of abortion facilities and infertility treatment varies widely between regions, as we have shown in the book. Furthermore, a recent report by the Committee of Public Accounts on Maternity Services shows perinatal mortality figures ranging from 5.1 per 1000 in Huntingdon and 5.3 per 1000 in Oxford, both relatively affluent areas, to 13.6 per 1000 in Bradford. They estimate that if all maternity units reached the same standard as the best, 4000 babies could be saved each year. Obviously, it is not so much medical intervention, but the material circumstances and well-being of the mother which affects the birth weight and chances of survival of a child.

The Brook Advisory Services (*The Guardian* 20 September 1990), commented on the rise in abortion. They highlighted two reasons for this. Firstly, fear of the health consequences of the Pill: 25 per cent of women in an Oxford survey had recently stopped using oral contraceptives. This underlines the call for more and better research into improved contraception. The other factor they highlighted was the economic difficulties which women would face if they lost their jobs as a result of pregnancy or to care for a baby.

The decline of British capitalism – continued

From the point of view of our ability to control our fertility and our lives in general, whatever the legal rights women have won, and whatever science and technology have made possible, the exercise of those rights, and the access to those innovations, are a different matter. All the different aspects of life in modern, capitalist Britain described above – reactionary ideology, Tory cuts on top of a shortage of resources, poverty and class oppression – all constrain the ability of women, especially working-class women, to exercise even the limited rights we have established.

What are the prospects for improving this situation? Thatcher's 'economic miracle' has been a success only for big business and the wealthy minority. Company profits have increased and so have the personal incomes of the rich. But this has been based on a redistribution of wealth to the rich from the rest of us, of which the poll tax is only the most recent and most hated example. Growth has been concentrated in the service sector where women workers, on low wages, in poor conditions and with few benefits and rights, are also concentrated. 'One-offs', such as the £87 billion in tax revenue from North Sea Oil, along with the sale of nationalised industries, have helped to give the illusion that the economy is going forward. In the meantime, one-fifth of manufacturing industry, on which all other sectors of the economy ultimately depend, has been destroyed. The underlying weakness of the British economy has been concealed by the growth in the world economy since 1981.

However, this boom in the UK and US economies is coming to an end. In Britain, inflation and high mortgages are threatening even more the living standards and conditions of the working-class and large sections of the middle class. This recession is being accompanied by a collapse in precisely the service sector which the Tories saw as the basis of its 'boom'. Bankruptcy and closure in retail businesses and design consultancies, lay-offs in financial firms and cutbacks by estate agents as a result of the collapse in the housing market, are announced weekly.

The crisis in the Middle East could trigger an international recession. High oil prices will open up a nightmare in the Third World, where, over the last ten years, the capitalist 'market' has in any case meant debt, poverty, starvation, disease and war. A world recession or slump will have a devastating effect on the British economy and will inevitably mean further attacks on the living standards and services of working-class people, especially women.

No issue can be resolved without taking into account the state of the society concerned. This is as true for infertility treatment as it is for any other service or treatment for which we campaign. Environmental pollution and unhealthy or unsafe working conditions are a contributory factor to infertility and miscarriage, as well as to perinatal and infant mortality. In a recession, where capitalism will cut corners even further, these will worsen.

Every demand for more research, better treatment facilities and improved health care comes up now against a common barrier: shortage of resources devoted to the NHS and related welfare services.

The source of these resources, public spending, comes either from taxation on big business or from individual (mainly working-class) tax-payers. Under Thatcher, big business has had a reduction in taxation and will resist any attempt to increase taxation on profits again, especially in a recession. On the other hand, increasing taxation from workers means cutting living standards and therefore contributing in other ways to ill health. Progressive taxation of the wealthy minority would, of course, be a welcome step in the direction of greater social equality. However, it has to be recognised that only ownership and control of the means of producing wealth, to allow for the distribution of goods and services on the basis of the real needs of the majority of the population, could provide the resources required to transform the lives of working people.

The labour movement and the Labour leaders

We have shown in this book how the battle, both to change traditional ideas and to increase facilities and raise living standards, has been carried out through the labour movement. As women have moved into the workforce, they have joined unions in increasing numbers and now dominate COHSE, NUPE, CPSA and USDAW. They increasingly see the labour movement as a legitimate vehicle for their demands. After all, a movement which purports to stand for improving the conditions of ordinary people, and which, in words at least, stands for a better society, should also stand for an improvement in all aspects of life for women, including the availability of the facilities which will allow them to control their own fertility.

The labour movement now officially stands for the right to birth control, abortion and infertility treatment. Much is said in speeches about the right of individuals to develop their full potential. But if this is to be translated into a reality, then policies have to be developed, campaigned on and implemented, to tackle the lack of resources and the lack of control by working people over their own lives and society generally.

Neither in boom nor slump has capitalism liberated women, but the current leadership of the Labour Party, divorced from the day-to-day life of the working class, have been completely taken in by Tory propaganda about the 'market'. They talk increasingly of postponing reforms and much needed increases in benefits to the poorest sections of society until the economy is 'back on its feet'.

Yet the lesson of the last Labour government of 1974-79 was that, within the limits of capitalism, no lasting reforms are possible. The situation facing the next Labour government, if Neil Kinnock replaces Thatcher, will be even worse than it was in 1974. Any government which attempts to manage the existing economic system will find itself being driven to carry out crisis measures in the interests of big business against the working class. The policies and conduct of Neil Kinnock and Roy Hattersley already make it clear that they intend to go down this path. In an interview at the start of the 1990 Labour Party conference, Hattersley remarked: 'There's not going to be a time when we (a future Labour government) create money or borrow money in huge amounts for consumer expenditure, which child benefits and increases in pensions of course are' (*The Independent* 2 October 1990).

However, a Labour government will face the opposition of workers if it attempts to carry out similar policies to those of Thatcher. In the ranks of the Labour Party, there is already concern at the lack of clear commitment on benefits and funding for the welfare state. Under Thatcher, the main opposition to cuts in the NHS has come from workers in the NHS such as nurses and ambulance workers, with the support of the vast majority of other workers. Only an inept and fearful leadership managed to snatch defeat from the jaws of victory.

The defeat of important sections of workers, like the miners, together with the lack of any lead from the trade union or Labour Party leaders, led many workers to resign themselves to waiting for the return of a Labour government. But when such a government is elected, regardless of the pathetically limited commitments of the Labour leaders, workers will demand action to reverse Tory cuts and improve workers' living standards and rights.

The need for socialist change

Major reforms such as the introduction of the NHS, improvements in living standards and municipal housing have been won through the struggle of organised labour in the past. Such a struggle is vital if past reforms are to be protected and new advances made. There is no question of 'waiting for socialism'. Socialists must always be ready to fight to defend past gains. Moreover, new gains can be made, even under adverse conditions, through struggle. Nevertheless, it has to be recognised that there is a limit to what can be achieved within the present system, and past achievements can be whittled away if control of the economy remains in private hands.

We cannot fundamentally change our control over our own fertility, the treatment available or our access to it, unless we also change wider social and economic relationships. This means changing the ownership and control of the economy. We support the nationalisation of the pharmaceutical industry under democratic workers' control and management, because this would enable us to make real decisions about what research is done, and guarantee the safety and quality of what is produced. It would also release resources for the NHS now creamed off in profits by private companies.

We support socialist planning, based on the social ownership of the 'commanding heights' of the economy. These are the biggest companies, the banks and the finance houses. Workers' control and management by elected representatives, who are subject to recall and replacement, and who have limitations on their salaries and expenses, would ensure that the economy and society generally were run in the interests of the working class.

A socialist plan of production would harness all the resources of society to the energy and inventiveness of the working class. This, in turn, would organise and produce the goods and services to solve the major problems now faced by men, women and children: such as good quality homes, schools, health facilities and nurseries, and plentiful supplies of food and other essentials. Without them, it is not possible to improve the lives of working-class people or to provide the material means to liberate women in a genuinely democratic society. Based on an abundance of the resources needed to meet everyone's basic needs, the best results of science and technology could become available to everyone. For the first time, women – and thus human society – would be able to have real control of their reproductive capacities.

Further reading

Reference notes in the text have been kept to a minimum. However, for readers who wish to read more about the issues, the most important sources of information – except for newspaper articles, which are too numerous to list – are given here.

Parliamentary papers

The Warnock Report
Officially entitled the *Report of the Committee of Inquiry into Human Fertilisation and Embryology* (Cmnd 9314), published in July 1984. The issues were subsequently debated in the House of Lords (Hansard: HL debate 31 October, 1984, c. 524-531 and c. 535-593) and in the House of Commons (Hansard: HC debate 23 November 1984, c. 528-544 and c. 547-590).

Legislation on human infertility services and embryo research
A Consultation Document (Cmnd 46), December 1986, published by the government to summarise views expressed and provide the basis for further consultation.

Human fertilisation and embryology: a framework for legislation
The White Paper (Cmnd 259) published by the government in November 1987. The proposals in this paper were debated in the House of Lords on 15 January 1988 (Hansard: HL c. 1450-1508). A further debate took place in the House of Commons on 4 February 1988 (Hansard: HC c. 1198-1259).

DEBATES on the Human Fertilisation and Embryology Bill in the House of Lords
6 February 1990 (HL c. 711-726, c. 739-768, c. 804-827); 8 February o73 1990 (HL c. 950-1000); 13 February 1990 (HL c. 1251-1271, c. 1282-1322, c. 1344-1370).

*DEBATES on the Human Fertilisation and Embryology Bill in
the House of Commons*
    23 April 1990 (HC c. 31-133); 24 April 1990 (HC c. 166-?);
    20 June 1990 (HC c. 933-1044); 21 June 1990 (HC c. 1134-
    1222).

Books and articles

ARDITTI, Rita and others: *Test tube women* (Pandora,
    1984).

BOYSON, Rhodes and others: *The defence of the family* (The
    Church Society, 1986).

BRINCENO, Louise: 'Avortement: le RU 486, une methode
    d'avenir?' *Cahiers du feminisme* No. 45,
    Summer 1988.

BRITISH PREGNANCY ADVISORY SERVICE: *Artifi-
    cial insemination* (Austy Press, 1984).

CENTRAL MANCHESTER COMMUNITY HEALTH
    COUNCIL: *Reports of a sub-committee on
    the Warnock Report* (1985).

CENTRAL MANCHESTER HEALTH AUTHORITY:
    *Reports of a sub-committee on the Warnock
    Report* (December, 1984).

DURHAM, Martin: 'The family, morality and the new
    right' *Parliamentary Affairs* Spring 1985.

THE ECONOMIST: 'France's abortion pill' (5 November
    1988).

FLOMAX, L: *The sexual politics of reproduction* (Gower,
    1985)

GORDON, Linda: *Woman's body, woman's right* (Penguin,
    1977).

GRANT, Ellen: *The bitter pill* (Corgi, 1985).

HARTMAN, Betsey: *Reproductive rights and wrongs* (Harper
    & Row, 1987).

JOWELL, R, WITHERSPOON, S & BROOK, L: *British
    social attitudes* (Gower, 1988).

KEVLES, Daniel J.: *In the name of eugenics* (Penguin, 1985).

KENNER, Charmian: *No time for women* (Pandora, 1985).

KINGMAN, Sharon: 'Drug company holds back on abor-
    tion pill', *New Scientist* 4 November
    1989.

LABOUR ABORTION RIGHTS CAMPAIGN: *Abortion,
    the struggle in the labour movement* (un-
    dated).

LABOUR LEAGUE OF WOMEN: Annual Conference agendas. *LABOUR WOMAN*, newspaper of the Labour League of Women for the inter-war period. Both are available from the Labour Party Library.

LEATHARD, Audrey: *The fight for family planning* (Macmillan, 1980).

COUNCIL for SCIENCE & SOCIETY: *Human procreation: ethical aspects of new techniques* (OUP, 1984)

PHILLIPS, Angela and RAKUSEN, Jill (Eds): *Our bodies our selves* — new edition (Penguin, 1989).

NEW STATESMAN AND SOCIETY 18 August 1989. Articles on recent attacks on the *Roe vs Wade* amendment to the US Constitution.

SEAL, Vivien: 'Contraception: the growth of a technology', in *Alice through the microscope*, edited by Brighton Women and Science Group (Virago, 1980).

SPALLONE, Patricia: *Beyond conception* (Macmillan, 1989).

SPRING RICE, Margery: *Working class wives* (Virago, 1981).

STANWORTH, Michelle (Ed): *Reproductive technologies* (Polity Press, 1987).

SUNDAY TIMES: 'How to buy a baby', 13 January 1985.

WEEKS, Jeffrey: *Sexuality and its discontents* (Routledge, 1985).

Theses

KENNER, Charmian: *The politics of married working class women's health care in Britain, 1918-1939*, M.Phil Thesis, University of Sussex, 1979.

SEAL, Vivien: *The relationships and links between academic research in steroid chemistry and the industrial development of steroid drugs*, Ph.D. Thesis, University of Manchester, 1975.

Index

Other titles from Fortress

The Unbroken Thread   Ted Grant

An invaluable collection of Marxist writings from the period
1938-83, charting the development of Marxist ideas through
the 1939-45 war, the rise of Stalinism in Eastern Europe, the
post-war boom, the colonial revolution and the crisis of
British capitalism.

608 pages   **hardback £11.95, paperback £6.95**

Liverpool - A City that dared to fight
Peter Taaffe & Tony Mulhearn

The story of the fight by Labour councillors against the Tory
government and the part played by *Militant*.
'A fascinating self portrait...told with imagery redolent of
Petrograd 1917.' *The Independent*.

528 pages   **hardback £14.95, paperback £6.95**

Out of the Night   Jan Valtin

A classic socialist autobiography of a German Communist
Party trade union activist, from the revolution of 1918 to the
prison camps of Nazism.

712 pages   **hardback £9.95**

Month of Revolution   Clare Doyle

Published on the 20th anniversary in 1988, this account of the
May 1968 events in France brings those tumultuous events to
life.

80 pages   **paperback £2.50**

The masses arise   Peter Taaffe

Two hundred years ago, after the French revolution, this book outlines its history, defending the Marxist interpretation of that revolution, and draws lessons for today's labour movement.

150 pages + chronology & index   paperback £4.95

Germany — from revolution to counter-revolution   Rob Sewell

Answering the questsion of how Hitlerism was able to triumph, this book not only covers the workers' movement from 1918 to 1933, but draws out the lessons for today.

96 pages   **paperback £2.50**

Towards a new revolution — workers of the Soviet Union speak

The authors of this book, Elizabeth Clarke and Richard Peters, visited Russia in October/November 1989. Their fascinating account tells of the feelings of the ordinary worker, striking miners, daily life in the streets, shortages and queues — all through the words of the people of the Soviet Union themselves.

136 pages + photographs   **paperback £4.95**